Serving the Allergic Guest:

Increasing Profit, Loyalty and Safety

What the Experts are Saying

"As both the president of a hotel chain that serves millions of guests and one of the millions of Americans that suffer from a food allergy, I am in the unique position to appreciate both sides of the fence. I can wholeheartedly endorse this book, whether you have allergies or not, because awareness is everyone's responsibility."
—Steven J. Belmonte, President & CEO, Ramada

"I completed your piece and found it well researched, lucid and helpful. As a practicing allergist with a busy practice in New York City, I am often confronted by patients with food allergies or parents with children with same who find themselves restricted in terms of where they can eat. We are blessed in this City by a variety of places to eat and foods to try, and a treatise such as yours helps them understand the overall approach to allergies and broaden their horizons. I would like to see restaurants take advantage of this wonderful piece."
—Paul Ehrlich, M.D., Allergist
  Assistant Clinical Professor of Pediatrics
  New York University School of Medicine

"And you thought feeding your normal customer was difficult. Joanne Schlosser lays it on the line as she discusses life threatening food allergies and how food service managers and employees should handle the special needs of those with allergies. She brings you real stories and situations of how to and how not to handle the dining restrictions and needs of those with food allergies. A must read book for those in the industry. You can only make one mistake with people with food allergies, so prepare your staff and yourself with the information that can make a more pleasant and worry free dining experience for someone with food allergies."
—Hal Axelrod, Director of Catering, Northmoor Country Club

"As an international traveler with food allergies as well as a customer service consultant to the hospitality industry, I found Ms. Schlosser's advice to hotels, restaurants, and catering services to be invaluable. Every commercial food service establishment, from the hot dog stand to the five-star fine dining room should educate their staff on how to serve the allergic guest. It's not only morally right—it's a brilliant service strategy for increasing customer loyalty!"
—Dr. Patricia Gangi, Principal Consultant,
   Cornerstone International

"Patients with severe food allergies must use extreme caution when dining out. I applaud this book as a way to teach the restaurant industry how to serve this unique market. Kudos to any restaurant that takes the time to train their staff in these important and potentially life saving steps. Your business should quickly grow based on word-of-mouth from grateful guests."
—Dr. Robert Hellmers, Arizona Allergy Associates
   Diplomate, American Board of Allergy and Immunology

"The intense responsibility of every team member in the food service industry to safeguard and protect the physical health of those they serve makes this a 'must read.' Protecting your guests and your profits is so simple with this book as your guide there should be no more excuses for ignorance."
—BethAnn Neynaber, President, Solutions Unlimited

"Finally a book to help bridge the gap between planners, guests, food servers and food preparation. Joanne takes a delicate subject out of the closet and lays it gently on the table. Thanks for the foundation for some powerful tools."
—Lynne Wellish, CMP, Director of Special Projects
   Phoenix Preparatory High Schools

Serving the Allergic Guest:
Increasing Profit, Loyalty and Safety

By Joanne Schlosser, MBA
President, Food Allergy Awareness Institute

Food Allergy
Awareness Institute
A Division of Dynamic Presentations, Inc.

5418 E. Anderson Dr., Scottsdale, AZ 85254
877-FDALRGY (877-332-5749)

Serving the Allergic Guest: Increasing Profit, Loyalty and Safety
By Joanne Schlosser, MBA
President, Food Allergy Awareness Institute

Cover design by Erika Diehl, Phoenix, AZ
Interior design by The Printed Page, Phoenix, AZ

Disclaimer

The information presented here can benefit you and your organization. It has been compiled from extensive research utilizing a variety of sources believed to be reliable and represents good professional judgment. The accuracy of the information is not guaranteed, nor is any responsibility assumed or implied by the Food Allergy Awareness Institute for any loss or damage resulting from inaccuracies or omissions. This is not the advice of an attorney or medical professional.

Joanne Schlosser, the Food Allergy Awareness Institute is not liable for any decisions or actions taken as a result of information presented here. The book is not designed to provide legal or medical advice. If you have specific legal or medical questions, please contact your legal counsel or an allergist.

Other Products by Scottsdale Press

Serving The Allergic Guest:
Increasing Profit, Loyalty & Safety Leader Guide
By Joanne Schlosser, MBA

Serving The Allergic Guest:
Increasing Profit, Loyalty & Safety Videotape
By Joanne Schlosser, MBA

Bright Ideas for a Better Life
By Joanne Schlosser, MBA

The G.I.F.T.S. of Joy
by BethAnn Neynaber

Published by Scottsdale Press
5418 E. Anderson Dr., Suite 200
Scottsdale, AZ 85254

Order Information

To order more copies of this book or to receive more information on other products, please call (888) 999-7582.

Acknowledgments

A special thank you to the following people: Hal Axelrod, Paul Anzini, Tim Casey, Inge Casey, Jeffrey Dashevsky, Dr. Paul Ehrlich, Dr. Patricia Gangi, Dr. Robert Hellmers, Steve Belmonte, Daniel Dodson, Anthony Marshall, Lori Newberg, Rick Diaz, Mary O'Connor, Matthew Reichel, Dr. Robert Reisman, Blake Rubeor, Gwen Salem, Robert Shcolnik, Joseph Silberschlag, Lynne Wellish, Allan Wiser. Information from them provided great insight.

Thanks also go to Joanne Stein for her editorial genius and writing assistance; Steve Elliott for compiling and analyzing the restaurant survey research; Kortney Watson for her research assistance; Nancy Katrakis, a great printer who meets impossible deadlines, and to Erika Diehl, who created the book cover design.

In addition thanks go to Rick Pontz for always being there for me; Tina Hochstetler, who provided encouragement and ideas to keep the project going; BethAnn Neynaber, who provided continuous inspiration, motivation and friendship, and Robin Petrowski for her guidance.

Dedication

*To my parents, Art and Elaine Schlosser, who raised me
to believe that one person can make a difference.
And especially for enduring thousands of hours of fear and
anguish over my childhood food allergies and related asthma.*

Foreword

I have been deathly allergic to pine nuts since I was a child and as is the case with most allergies, the effects only intensify with age. I have experienced nine attacks that resulted in anaphylactic shock and on the last occasion was paddled back to life after my heart stopped beating. Unfortunately, the horror of a near-death experience like this pales in comparison to the impending fear of being "poisoned."

Indeed, every near-fatal allergic reaction occurred while traveling, and as a hotelier, I travel extensively. I am a very animated person by nature and I go to extreme measures to explain my situation. Trust me, I do my part. I explain that any contact with pine nuts, even utensils that touched a food product made with pine nuts, will most likely kill me. My efforts, however, are in vain and 95 percent of the time I am met with blank stares.

Believe it or not, it is very difficult to avoid pine nuts since they are used in flavoring and hundreds of other food offerings such as soups, salads, sauces, cookies, pie crusts, breads, pastries, etc. Most recently, I was on an airplane and went through the whole spiel about being deathly allergic to pine nuts with the flight attendant. Her response, highlighted with an irritated wave of the hand, was "*Whatever. What do you want to drink?*" As it turned out, there were pine nuts in the entrée and thank God I didn't eat it. I would have no doubt died at 30,000 feet and the airline would be embroiled in a nasty and very public lawsuit (my wife has promised me that!).

Whether you have allergies or not, I urge you to read this comprehensive and very illuminating publication. Awareness is a two-way street.

Respectfully,

Steven J. Belmonte
President & CEO, Ramada

Table of Contents

Introduction
Why the Book Was Written

A severe allergy to egg was diagnosed while I was still in diapers. As a child, I was allergic to over 60 foods; some caused mild reactions and others created horrible asthma attacks, vomiting and more. There were countless times my parents raced to the emergency room because I couldn't breathe. It was terrifying. These attacks were triggered by something eaten during the day. I was hospitalized on three different occasions for a week each time, due to these severe asthma attacks.

Most children outgrow their food allergies. Many of mine were eliminated including milk, chicken, turkey, corn, and berries. It has made life somewhat simpler.

Many mothers in that era prepared home cooked meals for their highly allergic kids and packed school lunches filled with safe food. Mom was no exception. She should be nominated for sainthood for the thousands of extra meals she prepared just for me. Imagine working all day to prepare the Thanksgiving feast then having to make a hamburger for your allergic child, and oh yes, a separate stuffing that didn't touch the turkey or contain any allergens. She was truly amazing.

She read every food label trying to keep me healthy. Dad would however, periodically "experiment." He believed that allergies were "mind over matter" or that maybe I'd outgrown them. One bite of a cookie often resulted in a trip to the emergency room and a shot or two of adrenaline.

Today we have a society with many working parents and single parent households. Individuals and families dine in restaurants more often; and people with allergies are no exception. There has also been an increase in allergic reactions, which has triggered an increase in asthma and anaphylactic shock episodes over the past two decades. With highly allergic people dining out more often the stage is set for problems.

After living with food allergies for over 40 years, I have been searching for methods to help the restaurant industry and its guests enjoy a safe and pleasant dining experience. It pains me to hear about someone becoming ill from food allergies whether it's a simple stomachache, hives or severe anaphylaxis.

I'm on a mission to make a difference, to make the world a bit safer for those of us with food allergies. Along the way, the restaurants that implement these ideas will generate increased loyalty and profit. People talk about their dining experiences, good and bad. People with special needs from allergies to heart disease to vegetarians relish sharing news with one another. They are quick to recommend establishments that cater to them and equally fast to "roast" restaurants that don't treat them well or where they become ill.

Brighten someone's day by providing safe and caring service. You'll be delighted with the results.

> Joanne Schlosser
> President
> Food Allergy Awareness Institute

Chapter 1
What Are Food Allergies?
What Do We Need To Know?

"Help! This is an emergency. One of the guests in our res-taurant ate something that she's allergic to and is having an anaphylactic reaction. She's having difficulty breath-ing. Get here fast and bring epinephrine!"

Millions of Americans have food allergies, a few quite severe. As people dine out with increasing frequency, you need to be better prepared to accommodate these guests.

Dialing 911 to get help for a restaurant guest happens more often than you'd think. An estimated 100 to 200 people die each year from food allergy related anaphylaxis (pronounced ana-fill-axis). Another 2,500 require a visit to the hospital emergency room. More still administer an injection themselves and don't seek professional medical attention. Most of these incidents occur outside the home: in restaurants, schools, day care and other people's homes.

Often the cause of the medical emergency is a reaction to a food that's unknowingly eaten. The diner probably asked the food server about the contents of a menu item and was given inaccurate information. Food allergies are serious business. About 2% of American adults and 6% of children have diagnosed food allergies. For some people this is a life and death issue. Reactions occur in a variety of ways, including flu-like symptoms of stomach upset. Others can become violently ill and even go into anaphylactic shock and die within a very short time if they consume even one bite of the wrong food.

Sometimes people aren't even aware they have a food sensitivity. For example, Lori learned she was severely allergic to fish when her grandfather kissed her on the forehead after enjoying a fish dinner. Lori's forehead began to swell and she felt ill. After that terrifying experience she now knows that if she accidentally consumes even a small amount of fish her throat closes up, making breathing extremely difficult. Without immediate medication, she could die. She keeps an epinephrine injection and antihistamine pills with her at all times as a precaution.

When dining out Lori and other allergic diners want to know their meal is 100% safe. She doesn't do this to be "difficult" but to protect her own life. She's learned the hard way that anchovies (fish) are used in Caesar salad. Anchovies are found in Worcestershire sauce. Who would have thought that a famous snack mix containing Worcestershire sauce could be life threatening for somebody allergic to fish? Lori wants her server to take the time to guarantee that her meal will be "safe" and delicious.

The symptoms of anaphylaxis, no matter what the cause, can appear within one to fifteen minutes after eating the allergen. People with food allergies, or the parents of children with food sensitivity, usually know that the food causing this severe reaction should be strictly avoided.

The offending food is often an unseen ingredient in a dish that seems safe. In other instances, trace amounts of the offending food maybe have come in contact with an otherwise safe meal due to improper food handling or preparation. Water-soluble proteins leach onto any foods with which they come in contact. Most people who suffer fatal or near-fatal anaphylactic reactions did not know they were eating the deadly food. This adds to their terror of "what's wrong."

Food-induced anaphylaxis comes on quickly. People like Lori rely on foodservice professionals to understand what anaphylactic shock is, what they should do to assist diners with special dietary needs, what ingredients commonly cause food allergy reactions, and what to do if an incident occurs.

The first thing an employee in the foodservice industry needs to know is how to recognize if someone is suffering from a food-induced allergic reaction.

Common allergic symptoms include:

Skin
❖ Itching in and around the mouth (or other areas)
❖ Hives
❖ Swelling of the eyelids, lips, hands or feet

Respiratory
❖ Upper airway tightening
❖ Throat swelling
❖ Nasal congestion
❖ Asthma
❖ Shortness of breath

Gastrointestinal
- ❖ Cramps, heartburn,
- ❖ Nausea or vomiting
- ❖ Diarrhea or flatulence
- ❖ Bloating or belching

Cardiovascular
- ❖ Hypotension shock
- ❖ Loss of consciousness

Anaphylaxis

Have you ever had a meal you were dying for? That phrase usually translates as a positive, as a craving. People with food allergies could literally die from eating a microscopic amount of the wrong food.

Your mission, should you choose to accept it, is to educate yourself and your staff to prevent a crisis. A food allergen acts like poison to the affected person's system.

These common foods are most likely to cause food-induced anaphylaxis or other allergic reactions: peanuts, followed by tree nuts (including walnuts, Brazils, almonds, hazelnuts), milk, eggs, fish and soy. Peanuts and tree nuts account for 80% of the food-related anaphylactic reactions.

The first signs of food-induced anaphylaxis may look similar to a regular allergic reaction and then escalate. Symptoms include:

- ❖ Flushing of the skin, diner may feel warm.

- ❖ Light-headedness, drop in blood pressure

- ❖ Difficulty in swallowing or speaking

- ❖ Difficulty breathing due to severe asthma or throat swelling

❖ Cramps, vomiting, and diarrhea

❖ Swelling of the mouth and throat

❖ Hives, especially large hives

❖ Collapse and loss of consciousness.

❖ Death due to obstruction to breathing or extremely low blood pressure (anaphylactic shock)

These symptoms usually respond to medicine or treatment. In a few cases, symptoms persist and lead to death.

Anaphylaxis is much more severe than a normal allergic reaction. In a hypersensitive person, the immune system reacts differently to what is for most diners a harmless food substance. Even a small amount of the allergen releases chemicals within the body that cause the affected skin area to become red, itchy and swollen, blood vessels to widen and internal muscles to contract. Quite often a hypersensitive person also suffers from asthma which can be life threatening if not properly treated.

Medical attention is required immediately.

Meet the "Big Eight"

The most common allergens are:

❖ Eggs	❖ Milk
❖ Tree nuts	❖ Peanuts
❖ Fish	❖ Shellfish
❖ Soy	❖ Wheat

Medical reports cite these "big eight" as the contributors to 90% of food allergies. The remaining 10% are caused by 160 foods including melons, berries, zucchini, corn, chicken, and tomato. The "big eight" allergens are sometimes identified by other names in a recipe or on a list of ingredients. The server, (or designated contact) who is asked if there is wheat in an entree, needs to carefully check recipes and/or ingredient labels on packages of processed foods for these other names as well. Just because wheat isn't listed on the menu as being in the entrée, doesn't mean that it isn't in the sauce or the breading on a piece of chicken or fish. Wheat might be listed as gluten, farina or hydrolyzed vegetable protein. Just one bite of anything containing wheat makes someone who's highly allergic incredibly ill.

Here are the names that these allergens are known by. This list is thorough but does not promise to be comprehensive.

It is provided here because you can't keep a guest safe if you don't know all of the names for the foods that may make them ill. Looking at a package and reading only for "Milk" and ignoring the other 32 words containing dairy would be like putting up the roof on the convertible when it starts to rain and leaving all of the windows wide open.

A dietitian who spent most of her career working in a hospital kitchen said that she had never seen as comprehensive a list of terms. She acknowledged the hospital would have served its patients more safely and effectively if this information was available.

Natural flavors can contain anything natural including highly allergic substances. If a guest is severely allergic and "natural flavors" is listed as an ingredient, err on the side of safety and encourage the guest to choose another dish. For this reason, natural flavors will appear on each allergen list.

Eggs

People with an egg allergy need to avoid foods and drinks that have the following words as they contain or are made from egg:

Albumin	Egg, Whole or Dried
Egg White	Egg Yolk
Eggnog	Eggbeaters*
Egg Lecithin	Globulin
Mayonnaise	Ovalalbumin
Ovomucoid	Ovotillin
Livetin	Natural flavor
Micoparticulated protein product	

And similar egg products designed to remove cholesterol

A shiny glaze on yellow-colored baked goods usually indicates the presence of eggs. Many recipes use egg or egg wash. It's important to check recipes or packaging labels. Check batter, salad dressing, bread, breadcrumbs, breaded or batter fried foods, baked goods, croutons, pastry and coatings for starters. You find egg in the most unusual places. Various brands of mustard and horseradish contain egg or mayonnaise.

Check the following beverages to see if they contain egg products before serving to an egg allergic guest.

Eggnog
Pink lady
Some sweet and sour mixes
Some root beer
Some margarita mix

Milk   When reading recipes or pack-
aging labels, people allergic to
milk must avoid:

Artificial butter flavor	Butter
Butterfat	Buttermilk
Butter oil	Butyric acid
Calciferol	Calcium lactate
Caramel	Casein*
Caseinates**	Cheese
Chocolate	Cream
Curds	Dry milk solids
High protein flour	Ethyl lactate
Ferrous lactae	Lactalbumin
Lactalbumin phosphate	Lactose
Lactoglobulin	Margarine
Milkfat	

Milk (derivative, protein, solids, powder)

Protein concentrate	Rennet casein
Sour cream	Sour cream solids
Whey	Whey protein concentrate
Yogurt	Natural flavor

sometimes used to hold processed salmon, fish or meat together
**ammonium, calcium, magnesium, potassium and sodium*

Note: Frozen french fries may be coated with lactose for crispness.

Drinks that people with milk allergies need to avoid:

Alexander cocktails	Bailey's Irish Cream
Cassis	Eggnog
Grasshopper	Hot chocolate
Ice cream float	Milkshake
Mudslide	Smoothies
Sombrero or Kahlua & Cream	

It was thought that following kosher dietary law would help those individuals who are allergic to milk. By following religious specifications, foods labeled as "Pareve" are supposed to be milk-free and meat-free. In reality these products may contain a small amount of milk or dairy product due to trace contamination caused by airborne dust. "Pareve" labeled products may contain enough milk protein to cause an allergic reaction in those with a severe milk allergy.

Tree Nuts Some people who are allergic to tree nuts are also allergic to seeds and should avoid:

Walnut	Pecan
Almond	Almond paste
Macadamia	Pistachio
Hazelnut	Filbert
Brazil nut	Nougat
Marzipan	Hickory nuts
Cashew	Praline
Pine nut	Poppy seed
Pignolia	Sesame seed
Pinyon	Pumpkin seed
Chestnuts	Sunflower seed
Tahini	Natural flavor

The medical community does not agree whether oil produced from these nuts and seeds can trigger an allergic reaction. Err on the side of safety, if a nut oil is used in the meal, encourage the guest to make another allergen free selection.

Peanuts   People with sensitivity to peanuts need to avoid:

Peanut oil	Peanut butter
Peanut flour	Mixed nuts *
Natural flavor	

if they contain peanuts or were processed on the same equipment

Peanut butter is used in unusual ways including to thicken chili, flavor enchiladas, seal egg rolls and add flavor to cereals, baked goods and even Devil Dogs. It is a staple in many Thai dishes. Peanuts are commonly found in African, Chinese, Indonesian, and Vietnamese cuisine.

Because peanuts are the number one food allergen to cause anaphylaxis, a growing number of food manufacturers are going to great lengths to indicate if their product contains peanut or may have been processed on equipment that is also used to process food containing peanuts. This notification alerts the consumer of the possibility of cross-contamination and allows them to choose another product. Processed nuts, nut butters, and chocolate candy are especially susceptible.

Speaking of nuts, did you know that an estimated 1.1%, or close to 3 million Americans, have peanut or tree nut allergy according to a national random-digit dial telephone survey of 4,374 household representing 12,032 individuals. The study conducted by Hugh Sampson, M.D., Scott Sicherer, M.D., Wesley Burks, M.D. and Anne Munoz-Furlong shows that peanut and tree nut allergies are not rare and more should be done to educate patients, the public, and health and food service professionals about food allergies.

People are so highly allergic to peanuts that in 1999 the U.S Department of Transportation suggested that airlines set up peanut-free "buffer zones" when requested by allergic passengers. That means that at least one row in front of and one behind the affected individual would not be served peanuts on the flight. The peanut-free zone is meant to reduce the chances of minute particles of nuts becoming airborne and affecting the most allergy-prone passengers.

Now, when a passenger calls ahead and notifies the airline, the carrier often uses a substitute snack such as pretzels for the entire flight.

Fish

A fish allergic person needs to avoid the following ingredients:

Anchovy
Imitation shellfish
Caviar   Roe
Fish byproducts   Caesar salad
Calamari   Cod
Salmon   Trout
Herring   Sardine
Bass   Orange roughy
Swordfish   Tuna
Ahi   Mahi mahi
Halibut   Sushi
Worcestershire sauce   Natural flavor

Note: Thai cooking often uses fish sauce as an ingredient. Soups and stews may contain fish stock.

Shellfish According to the Mayo Clinic, the general category of "seafood" includes the list of shellfish and mollusks below. A person who is allergic to shellfish needs to exercise caution with the following foods:

Shellfish

Shrimp	Lobster
Crab	Crayfish

Mollusks

Clams	Scallops
Oyster	

Seafood

Mussels	Squid
Snail	
Natural flavor	

Note: Oil used to fry fish contains fish protein and could cause a reaction for a fish-allergic individual. If the oil used to fry fish is the same oil that's used to make french fries, it could spell disaster for a fish-allergic french fry eating guest.

The Mayo Clinic estimates that 250,000 Americans experience allergic reactions to fish and shellfish. Seafood allergies generally last a lifetime.

Wheat

People with a wheat allergy need to avoid foods containing any of the following: (For guests with Celiac Disease who must avoid gluten, see the list of Forbidden foods in Chapter 2)

Bran	Vital gluten
Enriched flour	Wheat bran
Farina	Wheat germ
Gluten	Wheat gluten
Graham flour	Wheat starch
High gluten flour	Whole wheat flour
Natural flavor	

❖ Hydrolyzed vegetable protein (HVP) may contain wheat.

❖ Certain brands of packaged shredded cheese are coated with wheat flour.

The following terms on a label may indicate the presence of wheat protein and should be avoided by the allergic diner:

Vegetable gum	Modified food starch
Modified starch	Gelatinized starch
Vegetable starch	

Soy   Anyone allergic to soy needs to avoid:

Miso	Soy protein isolate
Soy flour	Soy sauce
Soy nuts	Edamame
Soy protein	Tamari sauce
Teriyaki sauce	Tofu
Hydrolyzed plant protein	
Natural flavorings	Vegetable gum
Vegetable starches	Natural flavor
Textured vegetable protein (TVP)	

Hydrolyzed vegetable protein (HVP) may contain soy

Note: Vegetable broth may contain soy

Additional Allergens

The following foods don't cause as many problems as the "big eight" but you will have guests who ask you to verify if these ingredients are present in their desired meal.

- ❖ Corn   ❖ Alcohol
- ❖ MSG   ❖ Sulfites

Corn   Anybody allergic to corn needs to avoid anything with the word "corn" in it, except "corned beef" as well as:

Ascorbic acid	Dextrose
Dextrin (malto)	Di- and mono-glycerides
Excipients	Fructose
Gluconolactone	Glucose
Golden syrup	Invert syrup
Invert sugar	Malt
Malt syrup	Malt extract
Sorbitol	Worcestershire sauce
Natural flavor	

Hydrolyzed vegetable protein (HVP) may contain corn

Alcohol

A person who is sensitive to alcohol needs to avoid:

Beer	Champagne
Wine	Vodka
Rum	Sherry
Brandy	Cooking wine
Red Wine Vinegar	Cognac

Other known alcoholic beverages
Cooking Extracts that are not cooked or baked out such as vanilla

MSG

A person who is sensitive to monosodium glutamate needs to avoid:

MSG	Autolyzed yeast (extract)
Monosodium glutamate	Hydrolyzed protein
Sodium caseinate	Calcium caseinate
Gelatin	
Hydrolyzed vegetable protein	

In addition, these may contain MSG:

Textured protein
Carrageenan or vegetable gum
Seasonings or spices
Natural flavorings
Whey protein
Bouillon, broth or stock
Soy protein
Soy protein isolate or concentrate
Soy sauce or extract
Barley malt
Malt extract
Malt flavoring
Whey protein isolate or concentrate
Chicken, pork, beef and smoke flavorings

MSG or monosodium glutamate is a flavor enhancer. The U.S. Food and Drug Administration lists MSG as Generally Recognized as Safe (GRAS) for intake. A small percentage of people react negatively to the MSG typically found in Chinese food, canned vegetables, soups and processed meats.

Sulfites   People who are allergic to foods processed with sulfiting agents need to avoid:

Sulfur-dioxide	Inorganic sulfites
Vegetable fresheners	Potato whitening
Wine	Processed deli meats

Sulfites are used to preserve freshness and whiteness and to prevent spoilage of products. They may be found in everything from olives to wine. It is important to read labels on processed food to find out if sulfites are present. When in doubt, call the supplier and inquire because certain individuals suffer severely after consuming products processed with sulfiting agents.

Current laws in the United States prohibit the use of sulfites on fruits and vegetables in restaurants and require labeling of sulfites on prepackaged foods, drugs and alcoholic beverages. Unpackaged foods, including bulk food or food served in restaurants, should not contain sulfites unless a warning of their presence is clearly indicated.

The sulfite problem is a conversion of sulfites to sulfur dioxide which triggers asthma. While it is rare, sulfite induced asthma is reported in 3 to 8 percent of asthmatics. These infrequent reactions can be severe and potentially deadly.

Sulfites may be used to inhibit oxidation or browning of light colored fruits and vegetables such as dried fruits and dehydrated potatoes. They may also be used on lobster and shrimp to prevent melanosis or black spot.

Chapter 2
Celiac Disease and Other Special Dietary Needs

The current interest in health and wellness that's sweeping the country is impacting every age, ethnic and income group. You are seeing a growing number of diners with special dietary requirements.

These informed consumers want to spend their discretionary income in restaurants that willingly cater to their special needs. As baby boomers age, they are especially concerned about the quality of the food they eat. Food is considered preventive health medicine to this population.

While the Vegetarian Resource Group says the polls conducted in 1994 and 1997 show about 1% of the U.S. population is vegetarian, many signs indicate that carnivores are occasionally demanding meatless meals. A survey by *Restaurants and Institutions* indicated customers ordering vegetarian food tended to be between 18 and 33. Those who want vegetarian meals are more adventuresome and affluent diners. The National Restaurant Association's 1999 Tableservice Restaurant Trends report indicates that 90% of restaurants with an average check of $8 or more offer vegetarian entrees.

Other Dietary Needs

In the past few years, the number of people with food allergies has increased, as have the number of people who are watching their food intake carefully for other reasons.

Diners fighting heart disease may insist upon low salt or fat free meals. Other guests require high carbohydrate or high protein diets.

Religious convictions cause many Jewish, Hindu and Muslim guests to follow strict dietary laws. Knowing you can meet their needs will encourage these diners to favorably recommend you to their family and friends.

Millions of people have an intolerance to certain foods. This is more common than food allergy. Intolerance is a problem with the body's metabolism, not the immune system. The body can't effectively digest a portion of the offending food. *FDA Consumer Magazine* reported that about 80% of African-Americans have lactose intolerance, as do many people of Jewish, Oriental, Hispanic and Mediterranean origin. Intolerance intensifies with age.

According to Meeting Professionals International, special meals account for 2 to 30 percent of all banquet functions booked. Whether the need is for food allergy, dietary or religious reasons, the guest still wants tasty, satisfying food that will meet their specific needs. Catering professionals suggest providing as much notice as possible for special requests.

Genetically Modified Foods

The latest issue to hit the radar screen concerns diners who do not want to consume genetically modified ingredients. Keep abreast of what is going on. Alice Waters, owner of Chez Panisse in Berkeley, California, told food suppliers, "Flat out, no genetic engineering." She's given her staff a year-end deadline to go 100% genetically modified (GM)-free. At Seattle's hot Dahlia Lounge, Chef Matt Costello says his restaurant has eliminated most GM ingredients and is moving toward a total ban. In April 2000, 30 chefs held a press conference denouncing genetically modified food and demanding labeling of products containing GM ingredients.

Becoming GM-free is a difficult task, especially for a restaurant with hundreds of ingredients bought from dozens of suppliers. The change requires reading every label, then quizzing each supplier. New suppliers are found and/or recipes are adapted. Chez Panisse couldn't find an organic cornstarch and chose to eliminate it from dessert soufflé recipes. The biggest challenge is finding unmodified substitutes for common products that are often GM such as corn syrup, corn oil, chips, soda and bake mixes. A number of canola, corn, soy and some tomato crops are also GM.

Soybeans are often GM so concerned restaurants are moving away from soybean oil. Peanut oil may cause an allergic reaction. Corn oil is likely to be GM and; if not, it is expensive, it doesn't produce the best french fries or chicken wings.

The chefs who are against GM foods say, "We don't know the consequences on human beings. Europe is far ahead of us on this issue and they are right to resist these products."

Finding a restaurant that graciously handles special dietary needs can seem like a daunting challenge for people with food sensitivities or other dietary requirements. For example, Jean had a heart attack and now must follow a fat-free diet. She dreads going out to dinner because her options are so limited and the waitstaff usually treats her as if she's a nuisance rather than a valued guest.

Even heart healthy items like fish and chicken are off limits when restaurants sauté them or serve them with sauces and will not accommodate her dietary restrictions. Others have echoed her complaints. They wish restaurants would offer better options or more flexibility so they could dine out frequently and safely with friends, family members and business colleagues.

All it takes is awareness on the part of the chefs and managers and a desire to have repeat business from loyal guests.

For example, common preservatives like calcium propenate, bisulfites, and sodium benzoate cause allergic reactions in a very small percentage of diners. If a chef knows every ingredient and chemical that goes into the meal, he or she can knowledgeably help the wait staff and guest make safe choices. Health conscious chefs can choose to use citric acid to preserve fruit or lemon juice to stop oxidation of fresh sliced apples and bananas instead of a chemical. The chef may also decide not to use preservatives on fresh potatoes because it causes problems for preservative sensitive guests.

Whatever can be done to ensure that dining out is a pleasurable experience should be done. It's good for the guest and the restaurant.

Celiac Disease

If you've never heard of Celiac Disease, also called Celiac Sprue Disease, gluten sensitivity enteropathy or nontropical sprue you will soon. Celiac disease or Celiac for short, is a genetic digestive disorder triggered by the consumption of gluten, the protein found in all forms of wheat, barley rye and possibly oats. When an individual with Celiac eats gluten, the absorptive villi of the small intestine are damaged or destroyed, preventing the body from absorbing basic nutrients. Symptoms include abdominal pain and bloating, diarrhea, nausea, weight loss, anemia, dermatitis herpetiformis, fatigue and/or depression. In children it may result in the failure to thrive, vomiting, behavioral problems or irritability and unexplained weight loss and can lead to long-term complications such as anemia and nervous system disorders.

According to Dr. James Braly, author of *Food Allergy Relief*, in 1991 the University of Minnesota estimated that 1 in 5,000 Americans had Celiac disease. According to the University of Maryland School of Medicine's research in 2000, after testing 2,785 healthy adults 1 in 111 test positive for Celiac. After testing 1,505 healthy children, 1 in 167 tested positively. The Celiac Disease Foundation estimates Celiac affects 1:250 Americans. This would make Celiac disease twice as prevalent as Cystic Fybrosis, and Crohns disease combined. In Europe the numbers of people affected are similar. Improved testing has provided much new information in the past few years.

After contacting the Celiac Disease Foundation, the Celiac Sprue Association/United States of America and www.Celiac.com, it's interesting to note that the experts don't agree on everything necessary to keep a Celiac sufferer safe. The following information is provided as a starting point in the foods that are safe and forbidden in the Celiac diet. For more information on each of these fine organizations visit the References section at the end of this book.

Celiac Forbidden List

Abyssinian Hard (Wheat Triticum duran)

Alcohol (Spirits) *

Artificial Flavoring[6]

Baking Powder[2]

Barley Hordeum vulgare

Barley Malt

Beer

Bleached Flour

Blue Cheese (made with bread)

Bran

Bread Flour

Brown Flour

Bulgar (Bulgar Wheat/Nuts)

Bulgar Wheat

Calcium Caseinate ** (made outside USA)

Caramel Color[3]

Cereal Binding

Chilton

Citric Acid (made outside USA)

Couscous

Dextrins1

Durum Wheat Triticum

Edible Starch

Einkorn Wheat

Farina Graham

Filler

Fu (dried wheat gluten)

Germ

Glutamate (Free)**

Graham Flour

Granary Flour

Gravy Cubes [4]

Groats (barley, buckwheat or oats)**

Ground Spices [4]

Gum Base

Hard Wheat

Hydrolyzed Plant Protein (HPP)

Hydrolyzed Vegetable Protein (HVP)

Kamut (Pasta wheat)

Malt

Malt Extract

Malt Syrup

Malt Flavoring

Malt Vinegar

Miso[4]

Matzo Semolina

Modified Food Starch[4] (made outside USA)

Mono and Diglycerides[2]

MSG (Made outside USA)[4]

Mustard Powder [4]

Natural Flavoring[6]

Nuts, Wheat Oats Avena stativa

Pasta

Pearl Barley

Rice Malt (contains barley or Koji)

Rye

Semolina Triticum

Semolina

Shoyu (soy sauce)[4]

Small Spelt

Soba Noodles[4]

Sodium Caseinate (contains MSG)

Soy Sauce

Spirits (Specific Types)*

Spelt Triticum spelta

Starch (outside USA)

Stock Cubes[4]

Strong Flour

Suet in Packets

Tabbouleh

Teriyaki Sauce

Triticale X triticosecale

Udon (wheat noodles)
Vegetable Starch
Vinegars (Specific Types)
Vitamins[4]
Wheat Triticum aestivum
Wheat Nuts
Wheat, Abyssinian Hard
triticum durum

Wheat, Bulgar
Wheat Durum Triticum
Wheat Triticum mononoccum
Wheat Starch[5]
Wheat Germ
Whole-Meal Flour

Visit www.celiac.com to get links for specific alcohols that are forbidden and safe.

** *These are items where the Celiac Disease Foundation (CDF) and celiac.com disagree.*

CDF believes free glutamate is safe.
CDF believes buckwheat groats also known as kasha are safe.

[1]Dextrin is an incompletely hydrolyzed starch. It is prepared by dry heating corn, waxy maize, waxy milo, potato, arrowroot, WHEAT, rice, tapioca, or sago starches, or by dry heating the starches after: (1) Treatment with safe and suitable alkalis, acids, or pH control agents and (2) drying the acid or alkali treated starch. (1) Therefore, unless you know the source, you must avoid dextrin.
    May 1997 *Sprue-Nik News.*
    (1) Federal Register (4-1-96 Edition) 21CFR Ch.1, Section 184.12277.
    (2) Federal Register (4-1-96) 21 CFR. Ch.1, Section 184.1444

[2]Mono and diglycerides can contain a wheat carrier in the USA. While they are derivatives of fats, carbohydrate chains may be used as a binding substance in their preparation, which are usually corn or wheat, so this needs to be checked out with the manufacturer. Celiac Disease Foundation says consumer baking powder in US is safe, made from cornstarch base.

[3]The problem with caramel color is it may or may not contain gluten depending on how it is manufactured. In the U.S.A. caramel color must conform with the FDA standard of identity from 21CFR CH.1. This statute says: "the color additive caramel is the dark-brown liquid or solid material resulting from the carefully controlled heat treatment of the following food-grade carbohydrates: Dextrose (corn sugar), Invert sugar, Lactose (milk sugar), Malt syrup (usually from barley malt), Molasses (from cane), Starch Hydrolysates and fractions thereof (can include wheat), Sucrose (cane or beet)." Also, acids, alkalis and salts are listed as additives which may be employed to assist the caramelization process.

[4]Can utilize a gluten-containing grain or by-product in the manufacturing process, or as an ingredient.

[5]Most Celiac organizations in the USA and Canada do not believe that wheat starch is safe for Celiacs. In Europe, however, Codex Alimentarius Quality wheat starch is considered acceptable in the Celiac diet by most doctors and Celiac organizations. This is a higher quality of wheat starch than is generally available in the USA or Canada.

[6]According to 21 C.F.R. S 101,22(a)(3): "[t]he terms 'natural flavor' or 'natural flavoring' means the essential oil, oleoresin, essence or extractive, protein hydrolysate, distillate, or any product of roasting, heating or enzymolysis, which contains the flavoring constituents derived from a spice, fruit or fruit juice, vegetable or vegetable juice, edible yeast, herb, bark, bud, root, leaf or similar plant material, meat, seafood, poultry, eggs, dairy products, or fermentation products thereof, whose significant function in food is flavoring rather than nutritional."

Additional Celiac Concerns:

- ❖ Rice and soy beverages (i.e., Rice Dream), because their production process utilizes barley enzymes

- ❖ Cross-contamination between food store bins selling raw flours and grains (usually via the scoops)

- ❖ Wheat-bread crumbs in butter, jams, toaster, counter, etc.

- ❖ Cereals: most contain malt flavoring, or some other non-GF ingredient

- ❖ Sauce mixes and sauces (soy sauce, fish sauce, catsup, mustard, mayonnaise, etc.)

- ❖ Ice cream

- ❖ Packet & canned soups

- ❖ Dried meals and gravy mixes

- ❖ Grilled restaurant food—gluten contaminated grill

- ❖ Fried restaurant foods—gluten contaminated grease

- ❖ Ground spices—wheat flour is commonly used to prevent clumping

Provided by www.celiac.com and reviewed by the Celiac Disease Foundation.

Celiac Disease
Foundation

Celiac Safe List

Acacia Gum
Acorn Quercus
Alcohol (Spirits) *
Amaranth
Adzuki Bean
Agar
Almond Nut
Annatto
Apple Cider Vinegar
Arabic Gum
Arrowroot
Artichokes
Astragalus Gummifer
Baking Soda
Balsamic Vinegar
Beans
Bean, Adzuki
Bean, Hyacinth
Bean, Lentil
Bean, Mung
Bean Romano (Chickpea)
Bean Tepary
Besan
Bicarbonate of Soda
    (some contain gluten)
Buckwheat
Butter (beware of additives)
Carageenan Chondrus Crispus
Carob Bean
Carob Bean Gum
Carob Flour
Cassava Manihot Esculenta
Cellulose[1]
Cellulose Gum
Cheeses
    (except blue & chilton)
Chickpea
Corn

Corn Meal
Corn Flour
Cornstarch
Corn Syrup
Cowitch
Cowpea
Cream of Tartar
Distilled Vinegar
Eggs
Fish (fresh)
Flaked Rice
Flax
Fruit (including dried)
Gelatin
Gram flour (chick peas)
Grits, Corn
Guar Gum
Herbs
Hyacinth Bean
Job's Tears
Kasha (roasted buckwheat)
Kudzu Root Starch
Lentil
Locust Bean Gum
Maize
Maize Waxy
Maltodextrin[4]
Manioc
Masa Flour
Masa Harina
Meat (fresh)
Methyl Cellulose[2]
Milk
Millet
Milo
Mung Bean
Nuts (all except wheat nuts)
Oats[3]

28

Oils and Fats
Peas
Pea - Chick
Pea - Cow
Pea Flour
Pigeon Peas
Polenta
Potatoes
Potato Flour
Prinus
Psyllium
Quinoa
Ragi
Rape
Rice
Rice Flour
Rice Vinegar
Romano Bean (chickpea)
Sago Palm
Sago Flour
Saifun (bean threads)
Scotch Whisky
Seed – Sesame
Seed – Sunflower
Soba
(be sure it's 100% buckwheat)
Sorghum
Sorghum Flour
Soy

Soybean
Spices (pure)
Spirits (Specific Types) *
Starch (made in USA)
Sunflower Seed
Sweet Chestnut Flour
Tapioca
Tapioca Flour
Teff
Teff Flour
Tepary Bean
Tofu-Soya Curd
Tragacanth
Tragacanth Gum
Turmeric (Kurkuma)
Urad Beans
Urad Dal (peas) Vegetables
Urid flour
Vinegars (Specific Types)
Waxy Maize
Whey
White Vinegar
Wines
Wine Vinegars (& Balsamic)
Wild Rice
Xanthan Gum
Yam Flour
Yogurt

* Visit www.celiac.com to get links for specific alcohols that are forbidden and safe.

[1]Cellulose is a carbohydrate polymer of D-glucose. It is the structural material of plants, such as wood in trees. It contains no gluten protein.

[2]Methyl cellulose is a chemically modified form of cellulose that makes a good substitute for gluten in rice-based breads, etc.

[3]Cross-contamination with wheat is a slight possibility.

[4]Maltodextrin is prepared as a white powder or concentrated solution by partial hydrolysis of corn starch or potato starch with safe and suitable acids and enzymes. (1) Maltodextrin, when listed on food sold in the USA, must be (per FDA regulation) made from corn or potato. This rule does NOT apply to vitamin or mineral supplements and medications. (2) Donald Kasarda Ph.D., a research chemist specializing on grain proteins, of the United States Department of Agriculture, found that all maltodextrins in the USA are made from corn starch, using enzymes that are NOT derived from wheat, rye, barley, or oats. On that basis he believes that Celiacs need not be too concerned about maltodextrins, though he cautions that there is no guarantee that a manufacturer won't change their process to use wheat starch or a gluten-based enzyme in the future. (3) - May 1997 *Sprue-Nik News*
(1) Federal Register (4-1-96) 21 CFR. Ch.1, Section 184.1444
(2) "Additives Alert", an information sheet from the Greater Philadelphia Celiac Support Group, updated early in 1997. This specific information comes from Nancy Patin Falini, the dietitian advisor for the group and a speaker at a national Celiac conferences in the past few years.
(3) From the CELIAC Listserv archives, on the Internet, Donald D. Kasarda, posted November 6, 1996.

Chapter 3
How Diners Can Help Ensure Their Own Safety

You are the primary person responsible for your welfare. Be specific and forceful in the following. When asking questions to meet your health needs, state very clearly *"I have a severe food allergy and may become violently ill if I eat even a small bite of the offending food or substance."* If you are anaphylactic say, *"I am dangerously allergic to _____, and if I eat anything with even the tiniest trace of _____ I could die."* Then explain that they must also clean the utensils, pots, surfaces, etc. to keep you safe. Assume they don't know this and you need to carefully tell them how to best take care of you.

INSIST the server check to be absolutely positive a dish is safe before you place your order.

If the server seems uninformed, unclear or uncaring, politely request to speak to the manager or the chef to make sure your message is clearly conveyed. Realize that, especially during a busy meal-  time, the server and chef (or cook) may not be as thorough as during an off-peak time. The restaurant staff generally wants to do a good job, but it becomes a bit like the old game of "telephone" where you tell the server about the problem and by the time the kitchen gets the message, it sounds different.

Help the server to understand the severity of the problem. For example, many people realize quiche contains egg but most don't realize that creamy salad dressings are mayonnaise based and mayo contains egg. This small amount of egg can send highly allergic people into anaphylactic shock; it can make others violently ill. Tell the server, *"When I say 'no egg', I mean no mayo, no bread glazed with egg, absolutely no egg, egg white, egg yolk, egg wash, etc."*

If an employee doesn't know about ingredients or seems indifferent to your needs, ask to speak to the manager or the chef. Clearly describe your situation and ask for help in selecting a meal that meets your needs.

Give the server, manager or chef examples of what can be a problem and how to solve your problem. You are the expert; assume the restaurant staff is not. Tell them how to best meet your needs. For example, *"I'd like the cheeseburger but, if your buns are made with egg, then please serve the cheeseburger on a plate with no bun or bread."* Then, to make absolutely sure, say, *"And I don't want any mayonnaise or special sauce, either."* This clarifies to the server what to do and what the backup plan is. It will also prevent an additional delay of your meal when the server returns to say, *"All our buns and bread have egg."* This way your order and that of your dining companions can be filled more quickly. And you won't have to watch your friends eat their meals while you have to send yours sent back to the kitchen.

Never be embarrassed to ask for what you need. It's your health and possibly your life at stake. Carry a copy of *Serving the Allergic Guest: Increasing Profit, Loyalty, & Safety* with you and place it on the table when you arrive. Loan it to the server to show the chef. Highlight important sentences or paragraphs to make your points crystal clear. Tell them what page to look at to find the lesser known words for your particular allergen. This will help the restaurant staff to understand the severity of your allergy and keep you safe.

If you can't have wheat and really want eat at the local sandwich shop, bring your own rice bread and ask them to build your sandwich on it. In a few cities, restaurants are not allowed by law to bring "foreign contaminants" into a kitchen. This would mean anything they don't order. In that case you can have them bring you the sandwich fixings and you put it on your bread. Order a burger without the bun if you have a wheat or egg allergy or Celiac. You might be able to use a corn tortilla as an acceptable substitute. (Was this how the wrap sandwich was invented?)

If you are highly sensitive to certain foods like peanut, and the smell of peanut particles in the air may make you ill, you may choose not to eat in a restaurant that uses that product. A few people are so sensitive that they can become ill or risk anaphylactic shock from 1/44,000 of a peanut, which is smaller than one grain of salt.

If that's the case, you should always call a new restaurant ahead of time to determine if they use peanut, peanut butter, or peanut oil and avoid any restaurant that does. You may not want to risk eating there when the risk of cross-contamination can be life threatening. This may limit your dining options but will enhance your health and longevity.

To further ensure your health, learn brand names of certain products to determine which you can have, and which you must avoid. Restaurants often buy their meats, produce and canned and packaged goods from the same manufacturers so this can help when selecting your meal.

Particularly in fast-food restaurants, but also in other establishments, determine how the condiments are applied to a sandwich. If condiments are applied with a knife or spatula, the back of the ketchup spatula may have touched a sandwich laden with mayonnaise.  The spatula then goes back into the ketchup and contaminates it. By the end of the shift, the ketchup has white swirls in it. A tiny amount can be transferred to your sandwich causing an allergic reaction. When in doubt, order the sandwich dry and ask for packets of the condiment(s) you want or add your own at the table from a bottle.

A little safety goes a long way toward good health. When the kitchen staff cuts your sandwich in half the knife may not be thoroughly cleaned between sandwiches and cross-contamination may occur.

To be safe, specify that your sandwich is not to be cut. Cut it yourself. For the highly allergic, even if a knife is wiped clean, trace particles may remain. This microscopic amount can cause problems. It's always better to err on the side of safety.

A teenage girl died because she used a knife that had been wiped clean of peanut butter but still contained a smidgen of unseen residue.

If you haven't been to a particular restaurant in a while, ask about the ingredients. Occasionally, the recipe changes, the restaurant changes chefs, suppliers or products, and a menu item can go from being safe to being dangerous, or the reverse. A new chef trying to make her mark may change the ingredients in a sauce. The executive chef may start ordering product from a new supplier for better flavor or cost savings. If you haven't been to an establishment in the past six months, verify that your selection is still safe. This is one of the benefits of being a loyal customer. The staff gets to know you and your needs and works with you to keep you happy, nourished and healthy.

Most national chains standardize their products and suppliers to a large extent. Read the fine print. For example, on McDonald's ingredient list it says, "Slight variations may occur depending on the local supplier, the region of the country and the season of the year." **This means if your allergies are severe NEVER assume that because a menu item was safe in one city that it is safe in another.** Regional variations from local suppliers may also occur. When in doubt, ask.

When traveling for business or pleasure we may let down our guard because we are busy, preoccupied or adventuresome. The Mayo Clinic indicated that fatal reactions to food occur most often when people eat away from home.

Suppose you are highly allergic to fish. When choosing a restaurant you may want to avoid a seafood restaurant. There is too much opportunity for cross-contamination even if you order a salad and steak. The same cutting surface or grill may be used, which can cause problems for highly sensitive individuals. If you are very allergic to peanuts, avoid Thai restaurants serving peanut sauce and ice cream shops that use peanuts. Spicy food may also mask the immediate tingly sensation in your mouth from a nut allergy reaction.

If you have ever had an anaphylactic reaction or your allergies are very severe, you should always carry an injection of epinephrine, antihistamines and wear a medical emergency information bracelet.

Choose restaurants that prepare food from scratch instead of using prepackaged ingredients. When in doubt, your safest bet is to order plain, simple food such as salad, steak, grilled chicken, broiled fish, baked potato, etc. Eliminate sauces, salad dressings, desserts, anything that has the potential for an allergen or the opportunity to be cross-contaminated.

Again, your health is at stake, so don't hesitate to ask questions about the food you're going to eat. And, it never hurts to let the server, the chef and the manager know how much you appreciate their help in making your meal enjoyable. Let them know that you'll tell others about their willingness and ability to fulfill your special needs. This may encourage them to do even more for other people with food allergies or dietary restrictions.

When you experience great service, show your appreciation:

- ❖ Tip the server generously and tell her how much you really appreciate her extra efforts.

- ❖ Ask her to convey your appreciation to the chef or ask to thank him personally.

- ❖ Find the Manager on Duty or the General Manager and tell her how much you appreciate the special effort the staff put forth on your behalf. Let her know you'll be returning frequently (if this is true) because of their extra efforts and that you will spread the good word with enthusiasm.

People don't hear enough praise. They shine when you take the time to tell them they're doing something right. Be positively memorable and they'll remember to take great care of you on your next visit. If you really want to cause a stir, write a letter to the manager about your positive experience. It can be short and sweet but will make the employee or manager's day. See the sample on the next page.

Be loyal to those places that treat you well, make them your "second home" when dining out. Bring your family, friends and business colleagues to establishments that serve you well. The benefits are fabulous. The restaurant gets to know you and how best to keep you safe. They earn increased revenues, which enhances profits and helps to retain talented staff.

Date

Restaurant Manager
Restaurant
Street Address
City, State, Zip

Dear _____:

I just wanted to thank you and your staff for the delicious experience we had at your establishment (yesterday, today, at lunch). (I, my child) have a severe allergy to (fill in the blank) which can make dining out a difficult task instead of a delight.

Your staff from _____, *our server, to* _____, *the chef on duty, did a superstar job of:*

❖ *Checking the ingredients for our meal,*
❖ *Recommending something safe to eat*
❖ *Offering to make something special*
❖ *Making us something special*
❖ *Going to extra lengths to avoid cross-contamination*
❖ *Making us feel "special" not difficult*
❖ *(Insert your own thought)_____*

There are thousands of restaurants to chose from here in town. Yours made our experience pleasurable and safe. Thank you for taking the time to train your staff so well. We'll be back. And we'll tell our friends to visit you too.

Sincerely,

International Travel

When traveling abroad (or dealing with an international staff) Dr. Patricia Gangi of Cornerstone International, suggests carrying a 3x5 card translated into the local language which explains your food allergies and the severity of your illness when you eat the wrong item. The server then takes the card to the kitchen to make sure the chef receives the message correctly. Carry more than one card with you in case a server forgets to return it to you. (People also do this in the U.S. to make sure the server clearly communicates the issue and the danger to the kitchen.)

Jan McCall says, "Another idea for staying safe is to cut out a picture of the offending food or foods and use the international symbol for no, a red circle with a line running diagonally through it, to indicate this item can't be consumed even in small quantities. This should be incorporated with the appropriate words for maximum safety, so no one assumes you can't drink milk but could eat a dessert, sauce or salad dressing containing dairy."

The Mayo Clinic suggests you might want to learn enough of the language to name the foods that cause problems for you.

They also encourage you to plan ahead, especially when going overseas. Ask for medical advice that's specific to your destination. Also find the names of clinics or allergy specialists you can consult while traveling if necessary.

When traveling abroad, be sure to find out what other words to avoid. Ask lots of questions. **Don't eat anything if you aren't sure it is safe.**

These are a few of the words for "peanut" used around the world. This is not a comprehensive list. It serves as a starting point to facilitate your healthy travels.

In England
- ❖ Groundnut
- ❖ Monkeynut
- ❖ Arachis hypogea

French
- ❖ Pistache de terre
- ❖ Arachide
- ❖ Cacahouette
- ❖ Cacaouette

Dutch (Identical spelling in Flemish)
- ❖ Pinda (peanut butter is pindakaas)
- ❖ Aardnoot, aardnoten
- ❖ Apenoot

Esperanto
- ❖ Arakido

Finnish
- ❖ Maapähkinä (maapaaehkinae)

Frisian
- ❖ Apenút

German
- ❖ die Erdnuß (Erdnuss)

Viennese dialect
- ❖ Aschanti

Italian
- ❖ La arachide

Latin
- ❖ none, but botanical name is *arachis hypogaea*

Portuguese

❖ Amendoim, araquida

Spanish

❖ El cacahuate

Ask for restaurant recommendations from people who have traveled there. Contact the restaurants directly during non-peak times. Explain your food allergies and ask for recommended choices. You may find restaurants on the Internet. E-mail is a great way to communicate in advance.

Chapter 4
What Owners, Managers, Chefs and Servers Need to Know

Every employee who is involved with food service or food preparation needs to understand the basics of serving customers with special needs. Everyone needs to understand that this can be a life or death situation and to give the guest the information requested in a courteous and timely manner.

Employees need to understand that highly allergic people are so sensitive to peanut, shellfish or other foods that a single bite containing the allergen can KILL them. These people go into anaphylactic shock sometimes within seconds and can die within minutes if proper steps aren't taken immediately. The anaphylactic person is so sensitive that they can become ill or risk anaphylactic shock from 1/44,000 of a peanut, which is smaller

than one grain of salt. If you're a food server, acknowledge the importance of providing good information. Offer to check and report right back with an answer.

It's important for food servers to truly listen to what the guest is saying. Here's an example. At a banquet at a lovely resort hotel, the server was asked what was being served for lunch. The guest stated he has food allergies. The server responded that breaded duck was the main entrée. The guest said, *"I'm allergic to egg. Do you use egg in the breading or egg wash to make the breading stick to the duck?", "I don't know,"* was the server's reply and then she asked, *"Do you want to pick off the breading and just eat the duck?" "No."* he stated. *"Do you want a vegetarian plate?"* the server asked.

Around that time, the catering manager arrived and repeated the scenario. He too offered the guest a vegetarian plate. When asked to describe that meal, he told the guest it was pasta. The guest then asked, *"Isn't the pasta noodle made with egg?" "Oh yeah, probably,"* was the catering manager's response.

Guess he wasn't listening (or thinking) when told the guest was highly allergic to eggs. So after two strikes, they offered cheese enchiladas and a fruit plate. The irony is that if the server checked on the ingredients in the breaded duck, the guest might have been able to eat what was served. This would have saved everyone a lot of time and frustration.

At least one person on every shift must be designated responsible for knowing the ingredients of each recipe, packaged or outsourced product, or knowing where to quickly find out. It's better if more people are familiar with the ingredients but this person becomes "the" contact everyone comes to with questions or concerns so no one inadvertently checks with a less knowledgeable co-worker. The value of having two per shift ensures that even during busy meal times a knowledgeable individual can check on any concerns. There are a number of other names

for eggs, milk and other allergens. The contact person needs to know each of these to be absolutely certain an item is safe. See Chapter 1 for a listing of these "other names" for common allergens. Order a Food Allergy poster from the National Restaurant Association, to remind staff of the worst food allergens and what to do in an emergency. Better yet, order two as the reverse side is in Spanish. 800-424-5156. Post both. You may save a life.

Most restaurants and catering facilities use recipe cards to provide consistency. Keep yours in a handy place. Make sure it is accessible.

Recipes should always be documented and easily available. If a guest has a question about ingredients they can be shown the actual recipe. Never deviate from the recipe without making note of the change. Peanuts, nuts, shellfish, and eggs are a few dangerous foods that cause anaphylactic shock. If a recipe contains any of these items, the servers must be informed so they can encourage allergic diners to avoid these products.

You might want to create a three-ring notebook with recipes or ingredients lists. Create a separate section listing the ingredients for subcontracted items such as croutons, breads or prepared entrees. Cut the labels off the boxes, bags or containers and paste onto a standard recipe card. Keep one in the dining room and one in the kitchen. Or these can be typed up to look better.

Speaking of suppliers and subcontractors, there are people like Wade Myers, Operations Manager at Upper Crust Bakery in Phoenix, Arizona who happily provide any chef (or any other customer) with an ingredient declaration and/or nutritional information. Most operations are willing to help if you ask. If you consistently purchase items from a supplier, get an ingredient declaration or legend and keep it on file with all your recipes. This way you can cross-reference the bread to the sandwich ingredients, or the sauce to the chicken.

If you don't have this filing system handy, then have an easily accessible list of supplier phone numbers for bread, pastry, desserts or other items you outsource and call the manufacturer or vendor to get correct information if the customer requests it. Never guess!

If you can't reach the supplier, inform the customer of your efforts and encourage him to err on the side of safety and not eat the item in question. Recommend a safe alternative. Many supplier's operations are shut down during your busy evening hours; that's why having the ingredient legend on file allows you to best serve your guest. Once you reach a supplier, they may not have the answer readily available and will need to call you back. This again causes frustration and delay for the chef, the server, and the customer.

Whenever you order a new product, be sure to ask for the ingredient legend. Add it to your filing system and let the servers know if the new product contains any "big eight" item that might cause an allergic reaction in a guest.

Every employee should also be taught and encouraged to ask questions about the contents of a dish and where to find answers. **They never should assume they know the ingredients if they aren't 110% positive and if they haven't checked the ingredients recently.** It's far safer for all concerned to check. Recipes or suppliers change and the restaurant owners and managers doesn't want to be held liable for an illness or, worse yet, death because of an employee's fear of asking questions.

Here's what happens at a restaurant when there is no designated "contact person" or master list of ingredients. This is quite representative of what most people with food allergies experience.

Several friends were hungry so they stopped at a soup and salad chain hoping to get a quick and healthy meal. One automatically asked the person who was restocking the buffet if there was egg in the ingredients in the Thai Salad. The worker didn't seem to understand the question, so she brought another employee over. The guest asked him the same question. He understood, but didn't know the answer. He offered to ask another employee. The guest waited a few minutes and then saw him talking to the cashier so she went over to them. He informed the guest that the cashier didn't know either so she was going into the back storage area to find out. The guest asked, *"Since you are going back there any way, could you also find out if there is egg in any of the bread products."*

Twenty minutes later, the guest finally learned that all of the items in question contained egg. By now, the others in her party were finished with their meals and she hadn't even been able to complete the trip through the buffet. This is why it is important to have the information readily available. Not only is this guest and her party frustrated but if she is holding up the line, it irritates everyone behind her.

Excellent, knowledgeable service is provided at only a few of the national chains. The staff goes out of their way to be helpful. Positive stories like this get repeated time and again among people with special needs.

Pat tells us, I arrived at a Sweet Tomatoes restaurant and saw a Caesar Salad on the buffet line with a sign that said, 'contains no raw egg.' Most people would assume that meant that no egg was present. When you live with severe allergies and your life is potentially at stake, you must ask if there is any egg at all. The prepper didn't know so she asked a manager. The manager grabbed a notebook and proceeded to look up the ingredients. The manager then said, *"Well, there are no eggs in the ingredients except maybe in the croutons."*

Strike one. That is not an acceptable answer, I need to know if the salads contain any egg products or not." The manager sent the prepper to the kitchen for the box of croutons. She declared, *"Yes, I'm sorry, it does contain egg."*

Then she uttered the sweet sentence that created joy and loyalty. *"Would you like us to make up this salad for you without the croutons?"* WOW! Yeah, I can eat what everyone else is having without the risk of illness. It got even better, she asked, *"Is there anything else you would like me to check?"* Pat asked about the Chinese Chicken Salad ingredients. The manager instructed a staff member to prepare that salad without the fried noodles and suggested Pat continue through the line, stating that the special salads would be ready in a few minutes.

When Pat reached the end of the salad buffet, the staff was still working on her special salads and offered to bring the salads to the table. From the time she asked the initial question about the ingredients until the specially prepared salads arrived at the table, only 11 minutes elapsed. That's the kind of extra effort that makes people with special dietary needs return again and again. It's why you're hearing this story!

Once Pat received her portion, the restaurant worker can add the croutons and the noodles and serve the remaining salads to other guests.

Problem Prevention

While everyone needs to know how to call 911 and administer assistance, problem prevention is a far better strategy. When a customer inquires about the ingredients in a certain dish, the server should ask if the customer has any special food or preparation requirements. If they do, the server should immediately offer to check the ingredients and let the guest know if the item is safe for them to consume.

Too often the server assumes she knows the ingredients. Recently at a top ranked national chain restaurant, the server was asked if the boboli that came with the dinner contained egg. She said, *"I don't know."* After a quick trip to the kitchen, she reported that the boboli did contain egg. Sue ordered the meal minus the boboli, yet when it arrived the boboli was on the plate. The waitress came back to check on the meal, saw what had happened and said, *"Sorry, they shouldn't have put that on there."* True, so why did it happen?

The kitchen staff wasn't paying attention. The runner didn't compare the ticket to the meal.

Food Preparation

Kitchen staff must follow food preparation safety rules. A guest, who is allergic to fish and eats a piece of meat that was prepared or cooked on the same surface as fish, (without carefully cleaning the surface in between) may suffer an allergic reaction, as if they had eaten the forbidden substance.

You need to be aware of this at all times. A guest who is allergic to fish and orders a steak may never consider that the steak could come in contact with a grill or cutting board that has not been scoured free of fish. If possible, use separate cutting boards, knives, etc. to keep fish and seafood from cross contaminating surfaces used for beef or poultry.

It's also critical that utensils, pots, pans and cooking surfaces are kept spotless so no residue of the allergen remains to contaminate the allergic diner's food. And, when stocking the buffet, it's important to make sure the scrambled eggs don't spill over into the potatoes. This small amount of egg can cause an allergic person to become very ill if he or she eats the potatoes. If the serving spoons or tongs are accidentally used for a second food they should be removed and cleaned immediately. Health Safe Buffet System provides products to minimize cross-contamination and enhance the safety of your buffet.

Guests may suffer reactions ranging from stomachache to shortness of breath to nausea, throat constriction, flu-like symptoms, when an allergen is ingested. These symptoms may appear almost instantly after consuming as little as one bite of an item. To the allergic person it's as though you served poison. Their system automatically reacts as though it is fighting a war for its life. Reactions may take minutes or hours to develop. Symptoms can last a few hours or linger for days.

If a guest becomes ill, ask what you can do to assist him or her.

Check to see if the guest has an antihistamine or an inhaler that might help to alleviate the symptoms. If these are not providing relief he may want to use an Epi-Pen if he carries one. This is a pre-measured dose of epinephrine that can be administered immediately into the fleshy area of the person's thigh. It works even through clothing. In an emergency situation, one doctor said he actually walked around the restaurant asking if any patron had an Epi-Pen because he knew the suffering individual needed the injection faster than the emergency medical team could arrive. Thankfully, another guest did. This quick thinking action may have saved that guest's life.

Every employee in a restaurant needs to be trained to identify symptoms of anaphylaxis and allergic reactions. Employees need to be ready to call for emergency assistance if a diner appears to be exhibiting these symptoms.

Time is of the essence in this type of emergency situation and every phone in the facility should have the local emergency number (911) or local equivalent posted as well as the restaurant's address and direct phone number. Major cross-streets should be listed so that emergency personnel can quickly get to the site.

When talking to the 911 operator, the employee must describe the symptoms accurately and tell the operator that the guest is suffering from a severe allergic reaction to a food and may be anaphylactic. Tell the emergency team to bring epinephrine.

If someone is having difficulty breathing, first call 911, then notify a manager immediately. Sometimes you only have a few minutes before breathing stops or the guest loses consciousness.

In many hotel restaurants, the standard procedure is first to notify hotel security and let them handle the situation. If that is your policy, notify them immediately, clearly explain the situation, and if your security staff is not carrying epinephrine, suggest they call for emergency medical assistance now.

If a guest is having an allergic reaction, show compassion. Servers have made inappropriate comments like, *"Just because you got sick, doesn't mean you should tip me less."* Of course, he was the one who didn't check on the ingredients as requested, because he thought he knew the menu well.

After an incident where the paramedics were summoned, the server actually had the gall to say, *"Geez, people will do anything to get out of paying the bill."* She had no idea how sick that guest would be for the next 24 hours. If her manager was listening, he should have reprimanded her on the spot for such a moronic remark. Then she should have apologized to the guest.

Comments like that don't build goodwill or customer loyalty or motivate a customer to leave a tip. These servers don't belong in the hospitality industry; they aren't hospitable.

Guests rely on restaurant employees to keep them safe. If they are treated well and their special needs are handled without any hassle, they become very loyal and will continue to come back, bringing family and friends with them. Guests who get sick dish up lots of criticism, causing the restaurant to lose their business and that of the people they tell. Dissatisfied guests tell at least twice as many people as satisfied customers. The worse their physical condition, the more people they will tell. They want vengeance.

Play it safe, check with a chef or manager when a guest has a food allergy. Your guests will thank you and so will their families. By quickly and efficiently answering a guest's questions about the content of a meal, you can prevent a catastrophe from occurring, guarantee repeat business and earn a generous tip. If you or a loved one had a food allergy, isn't that the way you'd want the situation to be handled?

Now that you know the basics, let's break the information down by job functions within a restaurant.

What a Server Needs to Know

❖ When asked about ingredients, never say, "*I don't know*" or "*I think there is soy in that.*" The guest needs an THE correct answer. You get that by asking the chef or manager or looking up the ingredients. If you can't get an answer, advise the guest to make another selection. Always err on the side of safety.

❖ Don't pity the person or sympathize by saying, "*Oh that must be really awful.*" People don't want pity; they want good food and good service. You can positively say, "*I understand how important that is. I'll check on the contents of that dish and get right back to you.*"

❖ Walk the walk and talk the talk. Your eye contact with the guest and tone of voice should reflect your sincerity and concern with keeping the guest safe and meeting her needs.

❖ When a guest asks if the bread or rolls contain egg or are washed with egg, never say, "*All bread has egg.*" That response won't earn you a big tip because you're making the customer feel stupid for asking what they consider to be a life-saving question. The truth is that if all bread contained egg, the guest would have learned that a long time ago and wouldn't be asking now. If all the bread at your restaurant has egg, then say, "*I'm sorry, all our bread contains egg.*" Then ask if the diner or his companions have other questions. Once all the health related questions are answered, you're ready to take their order.

❖ When a guest informs the server that the diner has an allergy to a particular item, the thoughtful server asks, "*Are there any other foods you are allergic to?*" This way the server communicates these needs to the kitchen and the guest is safe and thrilled.

❖ One way to be sure the kitchen staff gives each special order a top priority is to write it up on a brightly-colored order slip or to write the word **SPECIAL** in bold letters at the top. This will ensure that, as it goes through the kitchen, everyone can easily see that this is a "special order" and won't mix it up with another or in any way cross-contaminate the meal.

❖ If the guest orders a Waldorf salad with no walnuts and says, "*I'm very allergic to walnuts. Please make sure there are no walnuts in my salad.*" the server needs to write up the order as, "*Waldorf salad NO Walnuts, SFA (severe food allergy)*" This will communicate the proper message to the kitchen staff. This does not mean you can remove the nuts and serve the salad. A fresh product must be created.

❖ Servers are busy. Occasionally a guest asks for decaffeinated coffee and there isn't a fresh pot made. You know they'll be leaving soon, so you hate to take the time and energy to make a fresh pot. It's so easy to just give the guest a cup of regular brew and pretend it's decaf.

It's been done, one server quit her job because of the "lack of ethics" of those around her who did things like this routinely. You might think, "*Oh, so maybe it will keep them up a few minutes. Big deal.*" Stop and realize that a few people can't have caffeine; they can go into cardiac arrest. All because you were too busy (or lazy) to make a fresh pot of decaf.

❖ Saving money is important, but there are times it doesn't make sense. Recently an employee at an ice cream shop was scooping up a vanilla cone for a guest. She noticed the bottom of the cone had a small hole. Rather than trash the cone or let it leak on the customer, she chose to fill the bottom of the cone with crushed peanuts to stop the ice cream from dripping through. The guest didn't see this and wasn't aware of the nuts until biting into them. A severe allergic reaction followed.

❖ The server or busser must be sure to clean each table, chair and booth thoroughly after each party leaves; especially if there has been a spill or mess made. Highly allergic guests could react negatively to a small amount of milk or other residue left on the table. A few people can break out in hives merely by splashing milk against their skin.

What the Restaurant Owner Needs to Know

You are ultimately responsible for everything that happens at your restaurant(s). You can delegate to your managers but if there is a problem, YOU will be the one held accountable.

Communicate clearly to your managers that this aspect of guest service and safety is a high priority. Make sure that managers are training new and existing staff on ways to safely serve guests with special dietary requirements. The education your employees receive may save a life. It will certainly benefit your bottom line with repeat visits from pleased patrons and new customers who've heard about your willingness to "do it their way." It may also be an asset when reviewing your liability insurance—see Chapter 8.

Empower and encourage your manager and employees to safely serve guests with food allergies, Celiac disease and other special dietary requirements. These issues are gaining visibility now and will become explosive in the next few years. Be proactive and gain loyalty and market share of these millions of diners.

Restaurants with good intentions are nice but if the staff does not have the training and tools needed they may trigger a guest's allergic reaction. Staff must refer to Chapter 1, carefully looking up other words for the ingredient the guest is allergic to. Or a manager or chef needs to do this for each of your locations and keep this information in a safe place that is easily accessible. Periodically check any packaged products or outside products to see if the ingredients have changed to protect your guests and your reputation.

What the Restaurant Manager Needs to Know

❖ Before learning anything new, most adults want to know, *"What's in it for me? Why do I need to know this?"* When you train your staff, make sure the chef, servers, kitchen help etc. understand both the liability issues when things go wrong and the kudos and loyalty that come from a job well done. If the possibility for additional compensation exists or if company profit sharing soars when sales increase, let them clearly see these tie-ins.

❖ If you can't communicate this to your staff you can't keep your guests safe. Call the Food Allergy Awareness Institute at (877) FDALRGY or (877) 332-5749 for training materials translated into other languages.

❖ You are responsible for everything that goes on in your restaurant. The better you work to educate your staff the more delighted your guests will be. To reinforce your efforts, post the "The Diner's Bill of Rights" shown on the next page, in a prominent place for the staff to view daily.

❖ If you can clearly convey these "3 C" keys to your staff you have the essence of safe service.

1. **Care about the guest**—listen carefully to the guest explain his needs and then do what it takes to meet or exceed his expectations.

2. **Check on ingredients when requested**—suggest a safe substitute if there is any doubt—use Chapter 1 to ensure you have searched for all possible variations of that allergen.

3. **Clean all necessary utensils, pots, pans, cooking and prep surfaces** immaculately before preparing a meal for a highly allergic guest.

If you want to WOW the guest, add step 4.

4. **Create.** Offer to create a special meal for the guest that may not be on the menu. Offer to use special prepackaged products that meet their unique needs. Guests are willing to wait a few minutes for a meal that is designed exclusively for them.

❖ Many U.S. aircraft are now equipped with adrenaline and Benadryl®. It's time for restaurants to consider doing the same. In your first aid kit keep an Epi-Pen. If you used it once, it would justify the price a thousand times over. What price do you put on a life?

The Diner's Bill of Rights

The right to enjoy a tasty meal in a public place.

The right to eat without fear of illness.

The right to receive pleasant, attentive service from knowledgeable staff.

The right to ask questions about the menu and food preparation.

The right to receive honest, accurate and timely answers.

The right to feel "special," not "difficult."

The right to have all dining needs met.

Joanne Schlosser, Food Allergy Awareness Institute
Jan. 1998. All rights reserved. (877) FD.ALRGY

❖ When a guest at the Berghoff Restaurant in Chicago tells the waitstaff he has a life threatening allergy or heart problem, it is mandatory for that guest to speak with the chef. The rule is "if in doubt, don't eat it." Once the order is taken the floor chef handles that meal. Guests are encouraged to communicate their needs—if the bowl must be scrubbed spotlessly before making an anchovy-less Caesar Salad, that's what will happen.

❖ Put systems and processes in place to ensure everyone knows what to do and does it.

❖ Purchase copies of *Serving The Allergic Guest: Increasing Profit, Loyalty & Safety* Leader Guide and Videotape. Call (877) 332-5749 to order. You'll find step-by-step instructions in how to effectively convey this information to your staff.

❖ Train all staff immediately, then train as new employees are hired.

❖ Review key concepts with staff semi-annually, perhaps at a staff meeting or as the menu changes.

❖ Be sure all kitchen surfaces are cleaned according to ServSafe procedures. Thoroughly scrub any surfaces, pots, pans, plates and utensils before using them to prepare an item for the highly allergic customer. Make sure the dishwasher and bussers feel they too are helping to keep guests happy and healthy. Remind the dishwasher why following the 3-part cleaning process is so important. Dirty silverware or plates can lead to cross-contamination. The same applies to all cooking and prepping surfaces.

❖ Consider using separate cutting boards and utensils for different items to avoid cross-contamination. A few facilities do that to maintain a kosher environment. The items for beef then could be color-coded so they are not ever used to cut, prepare or cook seafood.

❖ When a guest is presented food they are allergic to, the whole plate needs to be remade. You can't just take a tomato off a sandwich and re-serve it. The fact that the tomato touched the rest of the meal means it is contaminated from the customer's point of view. Many guests will want to keep the offensive plate in front of them until the new plate is brought to ensure that this doesn't happen. It's a matter of life or death to them. Even if this is against your normal policy, accommodate them.

❖ Guests can have an allergic reaction if the food they order is fried in the same oil as food that they are allergic to.

❖ One way to easily educate the staff is to use colored stickers on products to make them stand out. You could do this with the recipe book; a blue sticker means the item contains dairy, red means contains egg, yellow means wheat, etc. This way an employee could tell at a glance if the dish is safe for the guest.

❖ Colored dots or stickers could also be used on the shelves for canned goods and in the refrigerator or freezer to reinforce what is safe and what is unsafe for the allergic or dietary restricted guest.

❖ To find out exactly what ingredients are contained in products you purchase from suppliers, you'll need to ask the supplier. Many food manufacturers recognize their responsibility to label products adequately to meet the needs of allergic consumers. An easy form letter to the supplier's sales rep or corporate office should produce the information you seek. This should be sent on your letterhead. A sample letter follows.

Date

Sales Representative's name
Company name
Address
City, State, Zip

Dear (Sales Rep):

We at (your company name) are doing everything we can to safely serve our guests with food allergies and other special dietary needs. In order to do this, we need your full cooperation. Please review the list (below or attached) of products we purchase from you. We need to know which, if any, of these products contain egg, milk, wheat, gluten, corn, fish, soy, shellfish, peanuts, tree nuts and seeds.

Because each of these ingredients can also be identified by other names, you will need to check each ingredient and sub ingredient. It is imperative that verify which products contain known allergens to ensure a safe and pleasant experience for our customers.

If it is more convenient you may provide an ingredient label, ingredient declaration or legend for each item we purchase and our staff will review those for the above named allergens.

Additionally, we are making an effort to eliminate genetically modified products from our restaurant menu. Please identify any products on our list that may fit this description. Your recommended alternatives would be greatly appreciated.

Please provide this information at your earliest convenience but no later than (3-4 weeks). If you have any questions, I can be reached at _____.

We enjoy our business relationship with you and your firm and look forward to continued success together. Your cooperation in this endeavor will allow us to better serve our guests and is greatly appreciated.

Thank you in advance.

Sincerely,

Your name
Title

The other way to do this is to ask the supplier to provide you with a complete list of all ingredients, ingredient declaration or legend for every product you purchase. Then you can keep that information on file and you can compare the ingredient list to the allergen list to verify the safety of the product for your guests with special needs. It is reassuring for the guest to see the actual ingredient list.

Instruct your suppliers that every time they change ingredients in a product you purchase, you must be notified, so you can update your records. To stay up-to-date and out of hot water, send out this mailing on at least an annual basis .

What a Chef or Cook Needs to Know

❖ To safely serve guests with serious food allergies, the prep area and cooking surface must be thoroughly cleaned and sanitized. Remember that one bite of the wrong substance can kill a guest who has severe allergies. For those with extreme peanut allergy, a trace of peanut as small as a grain of salt can cause them to have an allergic reaction.

❖ The pots, pans, wok, grill, spatulas, spoons, plates, cutting boards, knives, prep area, etc. must all be completely free of the allergen to avoid the risk of cross-contamination. While this will take a few extra minutes, and may be inconvenient during a peak mealtime, realize that you literally have a life in your hands. Those extra seconds scouring the pan instead of casually wiping it clean may bring you a customer for life, instead of a lawsuit.

❖ A dish of ice cream can provoke tragedy. Using the same scooper for various flavors it is easy to contaminate the ice cream. Since peanuts and tree nuts are found in ice cream and are used as toppings, you need to be extremely careful. Milk allergic guests know to avoid ice cream. However, if a guest who orders sherbet may not think that the scoop or slab surface for "mix-ins" may be tainted with ice cream residue, or that small morsels of the ice cream or mix-ins may have fallen into the sherbet container causing an allergic reaction.

❖ If you really want to delight a guest with food allergies, there are special products that can be purchased. A few are listed here and more are mentioned in the Resource section at the back of the book. A quick search on the

Internet will produce suppliers of baking mixes with no wheat, no egg, etc. For example, Gillians Foods, 462 Proctor Ave., Revere MA 02151 (781) 286-4095 provides gluten-free, lactose-free rolls, bread crumbs, pizza dough and garlic bread. 'Cause You're Special Company, P.O. Box 316, Phillips, WI 54555, (815) 877-6722 www.causeyourespecial.com, provides gluten-free baking mixes.

❖ Glutenfreemall.com provides over 900 products from 20 vendors that contain gluten-free, wheat-free, soy-free, egg-free, dairy-free and casein-free foods at one Internet site.

❖ "Master Chef" is a computerized recipe system that can provide nutritional analysis, can print out and list ingredients, carbohydrates, fat, etc. This may be useful to those thinking about modifying their menus.

❖ There are many cookbooks that cater specifically to customers with food allergies. They can be found in libraries, bookstores and on the Internet.

❖ The *Dictionary of Food Ingredients* lists the components for various products and can be an invaluable reference tool.

Chapter 5
What Hotels and Caterers Need to Know

Hotel Restaurants

The information provided in the previous chapter applies to you.

Also, realize that many of your customers will be guests staying at your property. People traveling may be more at risk than normal because:

- ❖ They may experiment with regional cuisine.

- ❖ They may try dishes that they are unfamiliar with because they are on vacation or on a company expense account.

- ❖ They feel awkward asking about ingredients in front of a client or prospective account.

- ❖ They feel "bulletproof." "I'm on vacation, nothing can go wrong."

❖ They may trust that the server and kitchen know what they're doing.

❖ Familiar brands may not be available and they "assume" a food is safe.

Caterers

The information provided in the previous chapter also applies to you.

Whether the catering is done on premise or off, the guest's safety is in your hands.

Be proactive, encourage the meeting planner in charge of your event to let you know ahead of time if special meals are needed. Savvy conference planners are now printing the menus into the pre-conference agenda and the on site agenda.

Conference registration forms often allow for vegetarian preferences and also for other special dietary needs. Help your meeting planner help you to best serve the guests. Educate the planner to utilize these tips. This will prevent you from being besieged with a dozen last minute requests for special needs meals. With this information ahead of time, you can do a better job of preparing to ensure the happiness and good health of all present. This is particularly important if the event is off site, where your options at the last minute are limited.

When catering off site, make sure you know all ingredients used, or can find out quickly via phone. A guest who doesn't know if the food is safe may be tempted to try something, especially if you haven't provided an alternative meal and they are really hungry. If the guest becomes sick, you'll be blamed.

See the Delicious Service stories involving the Hyatt Regency Scottsdale, and the Arizona Biltmore in Chapter 6 for ideas on how to delight a guest with special needs.

Chapter 6
Delicious Service

Here are examples of what caring restaurants and caterers do to accommodate guests with special needs. Commit to delivering excellent service that meets or exceeds your guest's expectations. They'll think you're simply irresistible.

⌘⌘⌘⌘⌘

The Anaphylaxis Campaign suggests putting a note on the menu that says, "*Some of our dishes contain nuts. If you are allergic to nuts, please ask the server to suggest a nut-free meal.*" Another way to keep guests safe is to list nuts as an ingredient on the menu or reflect nuts in the name of the dish, for example, "*Pesto pasta with pine nuts.*"

⌘⌘⌘⌘⌘

Stock up on one or more cookbooks providing recipes that are geared to eliminate the "big eight" allergens. Check a bookstore or an online bookstore. *The Sensitive Gourmet—Imaginative*

Cooking without Dairy, Wheat or Gluten by Antoinette Savill might be a good start.

⌘⌘⌘⌘⌘

The Original Hoagie Shop in Tempe, Arizona, didn't know if their buns were made with egg. The counter clerk said, "*I don't think so, but would you like me to call the bakery and check?*" She asked the manager and he immediately called the bakery and verified that there was no egg. Juan could eat a tasty meal without having to worry about getting sick. Total time: 3 minutes.

⌘⌘⌘⌘⌘

A similar experience occurred at a California-based burger establishment on a Sunday afternoon. We asked if the buns contained egg and no one on premise knew. The cashier took the rest of the family's order then disappeared. Ron came to the table a few minutes later. This energetic 18-year-old said, "*I called our corporate customer service hot line to see if our buns have egg; and they don't.*" He flashed a huge smile and said, "*Would you like to come to the counter and order your burger?*" What a positive experience! Three years earlier (the last time trying that chain) no one knew and no one cared enough to find out.

⌘⌘⌘⌘⌘

People with allergies enjoy dessert too. Gentle Strength, a co-op bakery in Tempe, Arizona makes cakes for people with special needs, such as a wheat-less chocolate cake. And a baker at a Marie Callender's restaurant said to call ahead so that they can bake a pie without egg wash. To make sure the crust would still meet his high standards, the baker made 3 pies to see if milk, margarine or butter would work best to give the pie a lovely egg-free sheen. That baker became a real culinary hero. And he doubled sales. The customer was so delighted she bought two pies instead of one.

⌘⌘⌘⌘⌘

While attending a wedding reception at the Hyatt Regency Scottsdale, Robin asked the banquet manager to check the dinner's ingredients for anything made with egg, because of a severe allergy. He came back and said it would be taken care of and that she'd be able to have a delicious and safe meal. After Robin was seated, a server came over and verified that she would be receiving a special meal. She received a different salad, the same entree as the rest of the guests but without sauce and, a magnificent arrangement of fresh fruit for dessert.

Much to her delight, everyone's meal at the table was served simultaneously. Very often others are finished eating before a special request meal arrives. This makes the guest feel rushed, not wanting to keep the others in their party waiting. It also makes all the other diners uncomfortable as etiquette indicates they should wait until everyone is served before indulging. Robin was thrilled that the resort could accommodate her special needs on such short notice and has been back to dine in their restaurants as a result.

⌘⌘⌘⌘⌘

The Arizona Biltmore is another culinary hero! I attended a committee meeting and was surprised when dessert was served. Because the chef was notified in advance he prepared several egg-free desserts; one looked like chocolate mousse in a chocolate shell. I couldn't believe it! It looked so rich and so tempting. How could anything so decadent looking be egg-free? It was! Never before had a restaurant presented me with anything so incredible. The dessert tasted even better than it looked. That was decadently delicious service and will never be forgotten.

⌘⌘⌘⌘⌘

At "allergy friendly" restaurants, when a guest informs a server that the diner has an allergy to a particular item, the server is extra safe and asks, "*Are there any other foods you are allergic to?*" For example, eggs are in many items so I always ask about their presence. I'm also allergic to walnuts but, since they aren't found in many dishes and because the ones that do contain them usually mention it in the menu description, I rarely ask specifically about walnuts. However, twice in recent years I've gotten into trouble because I didn't ask and the walnuts weren't mentioned on the menu description.

The first incident happened when I inquired about whether there was egg in a roll that had sesame, sunflower, and poppy seeds sprinkled on top. The server said "no egg" so, delighted, I began to devour the roll. After two bites, I felt horrible, started twitching then realized the roll contained walnut pieces.

The same thing happened with a peach cobbler. It never occurred to me that walnuts might be present in the crust. When I asked the servers to check, each did their job and checked on exactly what was asked. At a restaurant where the staff is well-trained and where they know the dire consequences that an allergic reaction can cause, the server would have automatically gone the extra step to ask, "*Are there any other foods you are allergic to?*" I would have had a wonderful evening instead of a near death experience and the waitress would have received the best tip of her serving career. She could have made my day.

⌘⌘⌘⌘⌘

Two restaurant breakfasts, in the same week, but what a difference. Imagine going to breakfast with a business colleague, knowing that you can't have anything on the menu that contains egg, was cooked with egg or has been cross-contaminated by egg from a pan, grill, spoon or spatula. It makes life a bit tough. At each restaurant, I ordered the same thing, a "special" consisting of eggs, bacon and potatoes, minus the eggs. Usually this is less expensive than ordering a side of bacon and a side of potatoes. Restaurants usually serve the sides on two separate plates, which looks awkward, especially at a business breakfast. At the first restaurant, I asked, "*Would it be possible to add a few more potatoes since I won't be having the eggs?"* She immediately and emphatically said, "No." At the Hyatt Burlingame restaurant, Peter, an intelligent, creative server, offered to substitute fruit instead of the eggs to provide a balanced breakfast. What a great idea! He made my day and I made his.

⌘⌘⌘⌘⌘

Alan Dempsey, Vice President, Operations and Communication at Legal Sea Foods explained that employees at the front and back of the house receive training that includes allergy awareness. Typically the server goes to the chef with any menu-related allergy questions. If there is any doubt about a sub ingredient, the guest is encouraged to order another item.

⌘⌘⌘⌘⌘

Chili's Grill & Bar trains their servers for several shifts and also requires testing on menu knowledge. Manager Paul Anzini says new hires also work one-on-one with certified trainers to ensure the servers understand what it takes to do the job properly. If a guest tells the server they have a food allergy, the server is supposed to get the manager involved to make certain the guest's needs are met. Testing the system one day, a guest asked two questions about a menu item to see if it contained a particular allergen. The server returned with the correct answers and she anticipated a third question, she thought might be a problem, and came prepared with that answer as well. Kudos for thinking ahead to keep the customer safe.

⌘⌘⌘⌘⌘

Walt Disney World Restaurants delight in accommodating guests with food allergies and any other special needs such as those needing a gluten-free or kosher meal. Dealing with guests with food allergies and other special dietary needs is an everyday occurrence at Walt Disney World. In the restaurants he oversees at the Magic Kingdom, Executive Chef Rolf Gosswiler receives ten requests a day for special meals for allergic guests. He said ten years ago, they received only ten requests a year. They field countless requests for ingredients and for other special needs. The staff is trained to treat the guest with courtesy and respect and to make their experience palatable and pleasurable.

Specialty Chef Dan Kniola at the Grand Floridian Resort said, *"We will make items that are not usually served to accommodate our guests. We routinely stock rice milk, lactose milk, low-fat dressings and rice flour pasta on hand as well as many other items often requested by guests with special needs."* When the guest makes reservations at the property, they can tell the staff about any special needs and the kitchen can begin to assure a safe and delightful stay. Guests who do not provide advance notice are still graciously accommodated.

A little girl was highly allergic to shellfish. Her mom said if the fries were cooked in the same oil as shellfish or fish the girl would become quite ill. While many restaurants would say *"Sorry, maybe she better order mashed potatoes instead."* The Grand Floridian staff got a brand new pot out of inventory, heated fresh oil in it and cooked the girl's fries.

The Disney restaurants do not purchase monosodium glutamate (MSG) or peanut oil because many guests have negative reactions to these products. The Grand Floridian restaurants also have eliminated all but two items containing nuts from their buffets and those items clearly note they contain nuts. They replaced the peanut butter cookies and eliminated the walnuts from the chocolate chip cookies and the nut topping from the ice cream bar.

Each restaurant has one or more recipe books that are easily accessible to the servers. These are shown to the guest to answer any questions they have. If the product is pre-processed, staff can show them the container or box. If the product is prepared on-site, the guest can speak with the chef to ensure the food is safe. Disney really does want all its guests to have a Magical experience.

⌘⌘⌘⌘⌘

A luxury resort property in Scottsdale verified they too work hard to meet guest's needs by stocking soy milk and other "special" items. They reported requests for special meals, particularly because of allergies, are up significantly from just a few years ago. In their kitchen, the chefs are the managers and are responsible for any request for a special meal. While they prefer advance notice to best accommodate and delight a "special needs" guest, they are able to "whip up a thing or two" when a guest makes a request at mealtime.

⌘⌘⌘⌘⌘

One large chain's Director of Development said their training materials educate the staff to be on "allergy alert." The servers are taught about products that might cause an allergic reaction and taught what to do if one of the diners shows allergic symptoms. There are books located in various parts of the restaurant that provide a detailed description of menu items. When in doubt, the staff is trained to check the special allergy section. They see a definite benefit in providing this service; they receive lots of repeat and referral business from delighted guests.

⌘⌘⌘⌘⌘

There are roughly 14,000 restaurants in the New York City area—why does top-rated allergist Dr. Paul Ehrlich recommend Café Fiorellos? For starters, the restaurant provides a variety of food, much of it "healthy" including whole wheat pasta and a daily fish special that is generally poached and cooked oil-free. The menu says in essence, *"Please let the server know if you have any special requirements."* The staff encourages people with special dietary needs ranging from food allergies to salt-free, vegan, and so on, to advise the restaurant when they make their reservation. This information is then noted on the reservation. By calling ahead, Chef Pierre and his staff can work to create a delectable meal that meets the guest's needs.

They stock a huge antipasto bar with a large selection of vegetables and seafood. Many of the menu items are dairy-free which pleases milk-allergic, lactose-intolerant, and vegan diners.

Why do they bother? Obviously this takes some extra work and thought. Manager Mary O'Connor said, *"It's worth the effort because people really appreciate it. They come back time and again and they tell others."* Director of Sales Gwen Salem said, *"At all the Fireman Group Café Concepts restaurants the company philosophy is to 'be obsessive about hospitality.' What that means is taking care of guests in any way that we can when they are dining with us. If that means taking special steps to prepare their food, we do it."* They also provide menus in Braille and several foreign languages.

She continued, "Our first restaurant opened over 25 years ago. In a city where restaurants come and go it is important to differentiate yourself by the services you extend. The friends that we have made by being sensitive to special needs continue to dine with us. These people and their families will always dine with us, because we take care of them. If we were to add up all the revenue that these people and their families generated over the years, I could guarantee you it is substantial."

⌘⌘⌘⌘⌘

Executive Chef Lawrence Eells of the Hyatt Regency in San Diego modifies 20% of his banquet menus to accommodate guests' dietary or religious needs. One of the more unusual requests he received was for a low-fat, no wheat, no yeast, vegan meal. He did a lot of planning to ensure customer satisfaction and appreciated the meeting planner providing that information early. He also believes it is important for banquet captains to document all special meal requests to help with future planning.

⌘⌘⌘⌘⌘

Chef Eddie Matney, owner of the Epicurean Trio in Arizona says, "*Ninety percent of life is a struggle. Eating should not be a struggle. If we can't enjoy eating, what other pleasures are there in life?*" He's known for using lots of spices in his Middle Eastern cuisine. Chef Matney delights in creating food to meet special dietary needs. One night a woman told him she was allergic to garlic and shallots. "*What could she eat in his restaurant?*" "*Evian water*," he joked. Then he got to work and prepared her a garlic-free meal that keeps her coming back to his dining room.

Chapter 7
Disaster Stories and Liability Costs

Mistakes on the part of restaurant servers or other staff members can be very costly in terms of lawsuits and in the loss of goodwill and repeat business. Some of the plaintiffs in the following lawsuits received verdicts or settlements of six figures. Can your business afford the loss of dollars, time, and energy? Could you survive the negative press and potentially permanently tainted reputation?

⌘⌘⌘⌘⌘

A Philadelphia bakery settled a lawsuit against them for $100,000. Attorney Jeffrey Dashevsky represented a woman whose fiancé relied on the expertise of the bakery's counter staff. He told the employee his fiancée was highly allergic to peanuts and asked, *"Are there any peanuts in the brownies?"* He was told emphatically "no." After dinner, he served her a brownie. She consumed about ¼ inch of the brownie and immediately felt a tingling in her mouth. She recognized this as an allergic reaction and rushed to brush her teeth and mouth hoping to get any remnants of the allergen out of her system. Her throat began to constrict and she took two antihistamine tablets and attempted to induce vomiting. Despite a self-injection of an Epi-Pen into her thigh, she lost consciousness and went into anaphylactic shock. His family called 911 while her fiancé administered CPR. She was comatose in the Intensive Care Unit, then spent several more days in the hospital. Luckily no permanent brain damage occurred but she spent several months receiving psychiatric counseling. She became terrified to eat out and insisted on making her own food for her wedding. Her sister made all the food she ate on her honeymoon.

Meanwhile her fiancé learned from the baker that the brownie contained peanut oil and that the employee should have told him that. The lawsuit was resolved on the eve of the trial, almost 4 years after the episode.

The cost of the litigation and the negative local publicity add significantly to the damage done to the bakery's reputation for this mistake. **All personnel who are involved in food service must know how to find answers to guest's food related questions. Then once they know what to do, they must do it every single time, without exception.**

⌘⌘⌘⌘⌘

A 17-year-old died in England after eating a slice of lemon meringue pie containing peanuts. She knew she was allergic to peanuts but didn't think there would be any in the pie.

⌘⌘⌘⌘⌘

Athlete Ross Baillie of England died in June 1999 after eating a chicken sandwich containing nuts. His tragic death led to extensive media coverage of the problem of anaphylaxis in England.

⌘⌘⌘⌘⌘

A 14-year-old English boy died from a severe asthma attack after eating a snack containing a tiny amount of milk.

⌘⌘⌘⌘⌘

While I was editing this book in a restaurant, the server saw the title and became curious. Laura then stated that she was a respiratory therapist, moonlighting as a waitress. She said one day she was working in an Indiana emergency room when a woman came in who was very swollen and was having tremendous difficulty breathing. The triage team determined that she was anaphylactic and had accidentally eaten some mushrooms. She was highly allergic to mushrooms. They gave her an injection of epinephrine and her breathing resumed to normal within a few hours.

She later learned that when she explained her allergy to the server, he wrote down "veggie sandwich x mushrooms." Of course the chef seeing the "x" assumed that meant extra so he happily obliged, causing a near fatality.

⌘⌘⌘⌘⌘

Another case involves a woman who died after eating just a few bites of a chicken pesto sandwich at an Italian restaurant chain. She specifically asked the waitress if the sandwich had walnuts, indicating her life-threatening allergy. Allegedly, unbeknownst to the waitress, the chain had recently altered their recipe from pine nuts to walnuts. **A staff meeting and a memo explaining the change to all employees could have prevented this terrible situation.** The woman's family sued the restaurant chain for $10.4 million dollars. The case was settled out of court for an undisclosed amount. This incident has been cited countless times in national media. For some people, especially those with allergies, the company's reputation will forever be associated with this incident.

⌘⌘⌘⌘⌘

A 34-year-old man asked a waitress in a Chinese restaurant if the egg rolls were fried in peanut oil, citing his severe peanut allergy. She assured him that peanut oil was not used. He died 90 minutes later. No peanut oil was used, but the restaurant used peanut butter to seal the ends of the egg roll. This resulted in a $450,000 settlement.

⌘⌘⌘⌘⌘

In a similar case, a culinary school was ordered to pay damages of $434,000 to the family of a 27-year-old for negligence in his death. He ordered a vegetarian egg roll but was served one containing shrimp, which caused him to have a fatal allergic reaction.

⌘⌘⌘⌘⌘

A 23-year-old woman in Ohio picked up a chili dog and fries at a national quick service restaurant chain. Cinda took her meal home and, within minutes of finishing, she felt very ill; her stomach was rumbling and she started gasping for air. She told her husband to call 911 and then begged him *"Don't let me die."* After that, she collapsed into his arms. Cinda's face turned beet-red, then purple, then blue. At first she was convulsing every few seconds but then she stopped moving altogether. Her husband was terrified. It all happened so quickly. He thought, *"Oh my God, she's going to die."*

She almost did. When the paramedics arrived five minutes later, she was unconscious and barely breathing. Paramedics worked to resuscitate her but her airway was so swollen they had to try over and over before they finally pushed a breathing tube into her nose and down her windpipe. Cinda was rushed to the hospital in the ambulance with husband Jake following with their infant son. After several blocks, the ambulance turned the sirens on full blast and raced ahead. Jake was terrified. Cinda woke and in her confusion and terror, yanked out the breathing tube.

The emergency room doctors diagnosed anaphylaxis. All signs pointed to peanuts. The fries were cooked in peanut oil and there was the possibility of cross-contamination from the peanuts used for ice cream toppings.

Cinda says she won't eat at a restaurant now if it serves peanuts. For a year after the incident, she had panic attacks. Once something this frightening happens, you have to be vigilant every day for the rest of your life. The risks are huge. You can't begin to understand what it's like if you haven't had a first-hand experience.

This story was part of a three-page spread in *Good Housekeeping* magazine, February 2000, mentioning the restaurant's name and location. Imagine the negative publicity that generated.

⌘⌘⌘⌘⌘

A college student with a severe allergy to walnuts died after eating one bite of a "veggie burger." Because he had enjoyed "veggie burgers" in the past, he didn't bother to check the ingredients. This variety contained chopped walnuts. He called 911; they administered epinephrine but couldn't save him.

Are You Prepared?

After reading some of the following stories, ask yourself if your establishment would still be in business, or profitable this quarter, if someone sued because of the negligence of your staff. How would it affect your image in the community? Nationally? Is your staff prepared to handle special needs guests?

⌘ ⌘ ⌘ ⌘ ⌘

A couple was dining in a "theme restaurant" in Las Vegas. After a tasty meal, they decided to order dessert. He has an allergy to some tree nuts but not peanuts. The menu described the peanut butter pie as having "Bejoran nuts" as a garnish. The man asked the server what type of nuts those were. He was assured they were simply chopped peanuts.

With shock and horror, after three bites he began having a life threatening reaction to the dessert. The woman called the waiter to the table who still insisted the nuts were peanuts. The man's lips began to swell severely and his throat began to swell making breathing EXTREMELY difficult.

The server returned with the check—minus the dessert. The very nauseous man headed for the restroom. After returning to the table he thought it best to head to the nearest emergency room. Before leaving the restaurant, he felt the need for another trip to the men's room. When he emerged, he told the woman to notify hotel security that he needed immediate medical attention and would not be able to make it to the emergency room.

Hotel security arrived and this time he was escorted to the restroom where he was ill for a third time. His vital signs were monitored and the hospital EMT and fire rescue arrived. At this point he was given epinephrine intravenously. One EMT went into the kitchen and determined that the dessert garnish was "mixed nuts" not peanuts.

EMT transported the patient to the hospital where he remained for 5 hours, requiring additional care and observation. When the woman contacted the restaurant to arrange for "courtesy" transportation back to their car in the facility's parking lot, the staff hung up on her.

On her second call she was told "*we cannot send anyone for you because you would be a liability to the restaurant*" and then the employee hung up. Finally she contacted the assistant manager of the hotel who arranged for transportation.

The next day, after speaking with the corporate office for the restaurant, the man was contacted by the Director of Operations (DOO) for the local establishment. He apologized for the "unfortunate experience" and, after inquiring about the man's health, offered to pay for the medical costs. The man was still quite ill and didn't want to discuss it until he was feeling better and asked the DOO to call back the next day.

Three days after the incident, the man still wasn't back to full health. The longer he was ill, the more he wanted from the restaurant. The situation got ugly as the DOO said the restaurant was not liable for his experience. The incapacitated diner threatened to pursue monetary remedies through legal channels. He quickly discovered that the largest case pending was for $10.4 million and the smallest settlement was for $434,000.

The grapevine said that a similar "theme" restaurant settled a food allergy case out of court for $6 million. The man felt he was owed something and while he didn't die he went through terrible pain and suffering and the fear of death. The whole situation could have been avoided if someone had properly checked the ingredients. If the patron went into anaphylactic shock and died as a result of eating there, the property would face a huge lawsuit that it would probably lose due to staff error and negligence. The final outcome is not known.

⌘⌘⌘⌘⌘

The legal ramifications of not paying attention to a diner's requests aren't limited just to the allergic guest. A Mexican fast food restaurant in Lincoln, Nebraska, trains managers and employees to take time to be careful, especially with vegetarian orders. They do this because a local Hindu couple, who claimed to have found a piece of meat in a 59-cent cup of rice, sued them. Siva Rama Krishna Valluru and his wife Sailaja, both vegetarians since birth, sued the chain for $4,200 to return to India and receive purifying religious rituals. A judge denied the claim; saying they failed to show the rice was unwholesome or unfit for human consumption. Even though the restaurant didn't have to pay the claim, they may have lost business since the manager was well aware of the Hindu attitude toward meat. *"We have a number of Hindu students coming in from the nearby University of Nebraska."* They are now keeping a closer watch on all food orders. Lawsuits are costly, and demoralizing in terms of legal fees, court costs, management's time, negative publicity, etc. Even though the restaurant "won" the judgment, the negative publicity won't help sales.

⌘⌘⌘⌘⌘

In 1999, two American Muslims filed suit against a large casual dining operation, alleging they were served pork after requesting their orders be prepared in separate skillets to avoid contamination by pork products. Islam forbids the consumption of pork products. According to the suit, the customers found ham hidden under their eggs.

Daily Problems

The following stories didn't result in fatalities or lawsuits but are indicative of poor operations, management or service that occurs daily.

⌘⌘⌘⌘⌘

A server with a bad attitude at a popular tourist restaurant caused intense agony. The server was asked, "*Is the breaded shrimp made with egg?*" She left, returned to the table and said, "no." Feeling that the shrimp would be safe, the guest ate one shrimp coated with perhaps an ounce of beer batter and became very ill.

After just a few minutes, a severe reaction occurred. The guest's throat became itchy; she grew flush and was feeling nauseous. She vomited in the rest room. Her friends notified the manager who called the paramedics.

How sick would you have to be before you'd want paramedics to join your dinner table? Imagine the discomfort and embarrassment of having paramedics arrive at your dinner table, while other diners watched. They administered epinephrine and the woman's breathing became more stable and her color started to normalize.

The customers around the table were rather concerned and intrigued with the "floor show."

After the paramedics left, the manager returned and offered to comp the bill. To add insult to injury, the waitress who was serving the party then said, "*Some people will do anything to get out of paying the bill.*" **No one should ever have to go through that kind of physical pain and suffering, especially because a server, manager, or chef didn't take the time to check ingredients or prevent problems.**

The manager offered to pay medical bills, and invited the guest to come back for a meal on the house. No thanks! Not while the restaurant employs an untrained, uncaring staff. There was no guarantee or reassurance that guest wouldn't have another problem. Eating just one breaded shrimp caused all this havoc. (Several years earlier, the guest visited the same restaurant and had a similar disaster when the server didn't bother to check and the raspberry vinaigrette contained egg.)

The chef later said that he uses a single egg per gallon of batter. For somebody who has an acute sensitivity to eggs, even a microscopic amount of egg is like eating poison. When a guest tells you they are food allergic, pay close attention. It could mean the difference between good health and terrible sickness, possibly death.

⌘⌘⌘⌘⌘

A similar experience occurred at an upscale dining establishment. After suffering two allergic reactions there, it's a pleasure to know they are out of business. Having asked the waiter to check on our meal, he assured us he had. Within a few minutes of eating an appetizer, I became violently ill at the restaurant. Seeing my distress, the waiter then checked with the kitchen for a second time and determined that the appetizer contained nuts.

If you want repeat business and positive word of mouth about your restaurant, make sure your staff listens and acts when guests spell out their needs.

⌘⌘⌘⌘⌘

Food preferences vary around the country. A New Yorker assumed there was only one way to get a corned beef sandwich— on rye bread with mustard on the side. After asking about egg in the rye bread in a San Francisco café, he was assured it was safe. The corned beef sandwich came with mayonnaise slathered all over. This was not only an affront to the senses, but was life threatening to boot.

He pointed out to the server that mayonnaise contains eggs and that he was deathly allergic to eggs. He said, *"Remember how I asked if the bread had egg? Obviously, I wouldn't want mayonnaise."* The sullen server went back to the kitchen, changed the bread and brought the new sandwich back, mayo still clinging to the meat. The customer protested and the server said, *"We won't make a new sandwich; it was your fault for not ordering it without mayo."* The menu didn't say it came with mayo and no self-respecting New Yorker would ever dream of put mayonnaise on a corned beef sandwich. Never assume! When asking about bread or ordering a sandwich, ask if there is anything else that might cause a problem.

⌘⌘⌘⌘⌘

While dining at a large national hotel chain's restaurant, Tom had a similar horrible experience. The menu listed a steak stuffed with crab meat. It sounded delicious. The menu didn't elaborate further on the ingredients in the entrée and Tom didn't ask. It turns out, the crab meat was mixed with mayonnaise. When the problem was explained to the server, the same thing happened. The steak was taken to the kitchen, the inside was scraped out, and fresh crab meat inserted. The steak still contained traces of the mayo.

When a restaurant tries to save a few dollars, you not only lose a customer's business for life, but that customer will tell the story to countless others who may think twice about dining at your establishment.

⌘⌘⌘⌘⌘

While attending a banquet at the same property, Lisa asked the server to check the ingredients in the pasta primavera to see if it contained egg. She came back and enthusiastically reported there was no egg. Lisa became violently ill 20 minutes later, and the server was again found. This time after returning from the kitchen she said, *"Oh, I checked on the sauce but didn't check on the noodles."* Idiot!!! **When someone explains they have a food allergy you need a designated person to thoroughly check to make sure the meal is 100% safe.**

A banquet server waited with Lisa in the ladies room for an hour to make sure she would be OK. The manager called the following day and sent beautiful flowers with note of apology. Nice touch, but she won't eat there again. That was the second time she had a bad allergic reaction after asking them to keep her safe. Two strikes and you are out forever. It's not worth the risk to the highly allergic individual.

⌘⌘⌘⌘⌘

On two separate visits to a Chinese restaurant chain the server stated, *"We don't use egg or MSG."* Each was asked to check with the chef anyway to verify. Each came back and reported the dish contained "no egg or MSG."

Two visits with two different entrees, each time, I had severe chest pains and difficulty breathing for hours. I really liked the restaurant and wanted to be able to eat there safely so I called and spoke to the general manager who said very matter-of-factly, *"Oh, we use an egg wash on all of our meats and seafood to give it a nice sheen."* Why didn't the wait staff say so?

The general manager apologized and offered to send a $50 gift certificate to come back and "enjoy a meal." Based on what he said about all the menu items, I asked, *"What meal could I enjoy if they all have egg? Could a dish be served without the egg wash?"* He said, "No." He was not at all accommodating.

Believe it or not, the only dish available without egg was ground turkey and eggplant. We used the certificate, tried the eggplant and ground turkey and won't ever return.

Meantime, I've told countless people about the experience. Why go to a restaurant with an extensive menu if you can only choose one item on the menu? Why return to a place that doesn't teach its staff the fundamentals of listening to a customer and checking to keep the guest safe and happy? Why return to a restaurant that won't make even a minimal effort to accommodate its patrons with special needs?

⌘⌘⌘⌘⌘

Many Chinese restaurants say they don't add monosodium glutamate (MSG) but they use prepackaged sauces that contain MSG or hydrolyzed vegetable protein, which contains MSG. Some establishments also buy frozen lemon chicken or other dishes that contain MSG but, since their staff doesn't add MSG, they say they don't use it, or they say they don't add it, neglecting to say that the dish already contains MSG.

⌘⌘⌘⌘⌘

In 1997, the National Restaurant Association published a report saying, "The average cost of a single food poisoning outbreak in the United States in $75,000."

This figure includes medical expenses, lost wages, legal fees, and insurance premiums. Large court judgments are responsible for a good chunk of that $75,000. A point in case is a recent $800,000 judgment won by a California man against a restaurant after eating raw oysters, a known high-risk food.

The better restaurant employees are at establishing relationships, communicating and creating genuine partnerships between the diner and the dining establishment, the better they can avoid litigation. This can be accomplished by educating and training your staff.

Chapter 8
Reducing The Cost of Liability Insurance Through Training

A well known consultant in the restaurant industry thought I should call this book, *Kill Your Customer and Kill Your Business.* He felt that if your restaurant isn't doing a good job in keeping guests safe and happy, you won't be around for long. No amount of insurance will help if you continue to disregard your guests' dietary needs.

On the other hand, many restaurants are proactive and continuously find ways to serve better and reduce costs. Providing your employees with the knowledge and information necessary to do the job right will likely save you money on insurance.

The cost of liability insurance varies greatly with each restaurant. Communication and negotiation are essential elements. Insurance companies start with a base rate then adjust with surcharges and credits. Credits are based on favorable loss history.

Loss history evolves from effective employee training. Judgment credits are available to the underwriter and are based on risk evaluation, which includes a presentation of an effective loss control and training program.

Every restaurant should engage in risk management or loss control activities to make sure claims don't repeat. A proactive approach has a positive affect on the bottom line of the company. For example, according to Robert Shcolnik, with Harris/ Shcolnik & Associates, training employees to properly treat customers with food allergies will help to substantially decrease insurance premiums. This is especially true if the restaurant has had claims brought against them in the past. The agent can partially offset a negative claim history when informed that proactive safe food handling training, as well as allergic reaction prevention training has been provided to all employees. An effective employee manual, including training and risk management techniques, is a valuable tool in assisting your agent to obtain the best possible rate. If there have been no previous liability claims for allergies, depending on the market cycle and the industry, anything the restaurateur can do to show the insurance company your establishment won't have problems can help the agent get you a better rate. This equates to a healthier clientele, as well as a healthier bottom line.

Restaurant liability insurance increases if there are liability problems from falls, chipped teeth, allergic reactions, and so on. Most insurance carriers provide periodic computer reports with details of all losses. This is an excellent management tool, as it can give you direction for future training. In addition, certain carriers will provide posters, payroll stuffers, and other handouts to create employee awareness. Some carriers provide materials for safety meetings on other subjects to reduce injuries, slip and fall and the like. All such free material should be utilized, as it not only improves your safety, it gives your carrier a positive feeling about your management skills. This translates to lower rates.

It is important to have an open discussion on these issues with your insurance agent. As for the agent's evaluation and input, if you keep your agent in the loop, he or she will work harder for you. This gives you the opportunity to evaluate the experience and talent level of your agent.

Many of these recommendations have a similar effect on your Workers Compensation costs. Consider the following checklist:

❑ Give serious thought to a training and risk management plan.

❑ Convert your thoughts to a written form.

❑ Incorporate the written plan to an existing employee manual. If none exists, you can inexpensively develop one by seeking a template from a business-related bookstore or an office supply store.

❑ Train all existing staff.

❑ Develop a plan to train all newly hired staff.

❑ Select an experienced, qualified insurance agent.

❑ Provide copies of the above items to agent for proofreading and input.

❑ Ask the agent for help in obtaining free materials from the agent's carriers.

❑ Review your losses on a regular basis, watching carefully for repetition.

❑ Meet with your agent 60-90 days prior to each renewal to discuss the method of presentation that will obtain the best possible rates.

The larger your operation, the more locations, the more benefit training provides to control loss. The time spent training employees may save a life and save you money.

Serving the Allergic Guest

Chapter 9
Latex Glove Allergy Concerns for Kitchen Workers and Guests

New York, Florida and Minnesota have adopted rules that limit or prohibit direct-hand contact with food that will not be cooked before consumption. The intention is to reduce risk of contamination from dirty hands. Restaurant groups argue that if someone has dirty hands and puts on gloves they still risk contamination, and gloves must be changed between tasks which is as difficult to police as proper hand washing.

Curtis Hamann, President and CEO of SmartPractice, has done extensive research on the Natural Rubber Latex (NRL) allergy and has provided much the information contained in this chapter. NRL gloves have been used in the medical and dental fields for years. Extensive research has been done on the hypersensitivity of those wearing latex gloves for prolonged periods of time at work. A few employees are allergic or suffer from irritant dermatitis. Reactions range from mild burning, itching, and stinging to severe anaphylaxis shock and fatalities.

Anaphylaxis to natural rubber latex (surgical gloves) was first reported in 1984; since then, 15 deaths and thousands of injuries have been attributed to NRL and reported to the FDA. Latex sensitive individuals can have adverse reactions with as little as one part per billion of NRL.

Studies in the United States indicate 5-9% of the NRL-wearing population is allergic to the gloves. Avoidance of latex gloves is the safest strategy for these individuals. Some individuals can use gloves that have a lower level of the allergen. Others need to use vinyl or other non-NRL gloves.

Staff members and diners who are allergic to NRL may display an allergic reaction to avocado, banana, peach, potato, grape, tomato, fig, papaya, melon, kiwi, and chestnut. People with an allergic history to these foods may have a higher risk for developing NRL sensitivity. Symptoms may include edema, urticaria, oral pruritus, rhinitis, asthma, and anaphylaxis.

A newer problem concerns the impact of an employee properly wearing latex gloves transferring the latex protein to the food (causing the diner an allergic reaction). Some customers who have a natural rubber latex allergy have complained of symptoms after eating food handled by workers wearing NRL gloves.

So far guests have reported no documented cases of severe allergic reactions, but this remains a possibility, particularly for those with intense allergies to latex. Individuals who are acutely sensitive can have reactions when exposed to a parts-per-billion concentration of latex. These quantities could conceivably leach from the latex glove of a food handler into the prepared food.

Because some guests are so extremely allergic to latex, the mere thought that someone is handling their food with latex gloves is enough for them to feel ill. They fear that even a small amount of the latex powder becoming airborne and landing on their food may adversely affect them. They want to do whatever they can to protect their own health. If a guest asks you to prepare the food without latex gloves, please accommodate them. You have two options: Keep a box of non-latex gloves (such as vinyl, plastic or polyurethane) available or have the server remove his gloves, scrub his hands with antibacterial soap and then prepare the guest's meal. Honoring the guest's request is best for everyone.

Chapter 10
Show Me the Money

The question may really be, *"Do you want to earn more profits, generate repeat business, gain customer loyalty and increase word-of-mouth business?"* If "yes" make sure that your allergic diner and others with special needs have a wonderful experience because special needs guests can have a very positive effect on the success of your business.

The Food Allergy Awareness Institute surveyed diners with and without food allergies to determine their restaurant dining preferences. Seventy-five percent of the food allergic participants dined out a minimum of four times in the previous 30 days, 45% dined out more than 7 times in the previous 30 days. All of the other diners ate out at least four times in the previous month.

74% of the allergic respondents said they prefer to eat at restaurants they've been to before. Only 45% of the non-allergic diners were as loyal.

Loyalty is critical. When asked, *"How satisfied are you when it comes to your favorite restaurant meeting the needs of the allergic diner?"*

Respondents said:

35% very satisfied
43% somewhat satisfied
16% neither
2% dissatisfied
4% very dissatisfied

When asked, *"How satisfied do you think people are when it comes to the average restaurant meeting the needs of the allergic diner?"* the results were fascinating.

Respondents said:

0% very satisfied
24% somewhat satisfied
15% neither
38% dissatisfied
24% very dissatisfied

On a 1 to 6 scale where 6 is most important, rate the following when choosing a restaurant.

Group	Cleanliness	Service	Server knows ingredients	Type of food	Meets specific dietary needs	Makes special dishes	Location
Allergy	5.5	5.1	5.1	5.0	4.9	4.5	4.0
Non-allergy	5.7	5.2	n/a	5.0	3.2	n/a	4.1

Group	Always go there	Recommendation	Price	Good for kids	Quiet without kids	Coupon	Good low fat dishes	Good Veggie dishes
Allergy	3.8	3.7	3.6	3.4	2.4	2.2	n/a	n/a
Non-allergy	4.0	4.1	4.1	3.4	3.2	2.8	2.9	2.3

For those with food allergies, the server knowing the ingredients and the chef making special dishes to meet their needs far outweigh price, coupons and most other factors. This is where you build lifelong loyalty.

On a 1 to 6 scale where 6 is very important, rate the following as reasons for not returning.

Group	Dislike food	Too smoky	Someone got sick	Couldn't serve dietary needs	Not clean	Rude service
Allergy	5.7	5.5	5.4	5.4	5.4	5.4
Non-allergy	5.6	5.6	n/a	2.9	5.8	5.7

Group	Slow service	Wait too long	Not kid friendly	Too expensive	Too noisy	Location
Allergy	5.7	5.5	5.4	5.4	5.4	5.4
Non-allergy	5.6	5.6	n/a	2.9	5.8	5.7

People are not returning because they got sick or you didn't meet their dietary needs. Taking a bit of extra time to train the staff on how to safely serve these guests could win you lots of repeat business and enough bucks for a bonus check.

What could restaurants do to serve you better?
(Multiple responses were encouraged.)

84%	Train the servers on the problems of food allergies
80%	Train the servers to know menu ingredient
79%	Train the servers to always check ingredients
79%	Train all staff on the problems of food allergies
79%	Offer a variety of foods safe for me to eat
79%	Smoke free environment
70%	Offer to make something special
68%	Make something special if it is requested
68%	Customer service training for staff
45%	Learn my food allergy needs so I'll return
27%	Know my name, habits desires and needs

If you want to cater to this target market, these tidbits are telling you what it takes to win their business.

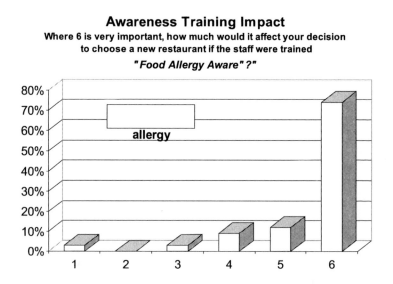

Awareness Training Impact
Where 6 is very important, how much would it affect your decision
to choose a new restaurant if the staff were trained
"Food Allergy Aware"?"

Overwhelmingly, people felt they would be much safer dining in an establishment that took the time and energy to train all staff members on the needs of food allergic guests. If your restaurant or food service operation would benefit from this type of training then call the Food Allergy Awareness Institute at (877) 332-5749 for a management course or a train the trainer program or purchase the *Serving The Allergic Guest: Increasing Profit, Loyalty, & Safety* Training Kit. The kits provide step-by-step instructions conveying the needed information to your staff in a fun and effective way along with a 13 minute video to reinforce the message.

❖ Train all staff immediately, then train new employees when hired.

❖ Review key concepts with staff semi-annually, perhaps at a staff meeting or as the menu changes.

Biography magazine asked readers:

"Do you think restaurants should be required to clearly label dishes that contain allergy-causing ingredients like peanuts and shrimp?"

84% said yes
16% said no

If you don't want to be told how to run your business then find ways to voluntarily comply to keep guests safe.

"When you dine out with friends, who chooses the restaurant?"

92% of the time the allergic person chooses or a mutual decision is made. These people are significant influences on the dining dollar. They choose locations for themselves, family, friends and business associates. People ask the person with allergies, to choose a location where they feel comfortable and safe.

Diners with special needs are also encouraged to choose the meal location.

Loyal customers love to promote someone who treats them well. As competition for the customer's dining dollar intensifies, it becomes more important than ever to create special long-term relationships with your key customers. *The Wall Street Journal* reported that, **"Long term customers spend more, refer new business and contribute to greater employee morale and stability."** In many industries up to 75% of the business is dependent upon repeat customers and referrals.

⌘⌘⌘⌘⌘

My sister and her family frequently dine at Acapulco, a Mexican restaurant in Laguna Niguel, California. They always ask to be seated in Javier's section. Why? Because he treats her three young sons like they are "the big cheese." In addition to the balloons that the restaurant provides, Javier has learned these boys love maraschino cherries. One small complementary glass of cherries per visit earns him a well above average tip. It also helps young kids behave well in a restaurant by providing something fun to do. But that's not all; he always suggests specials he thinks they would enjoy and does it all with a friendly, attentive attitude.

When she's making plans with friends and family, she's quick to suggest they dine at Acapulco.

⌘⌘⌘⌘⌘

Frederick Reichheld, in *The Loyalty Effect: The Hidden Force Behind Growth, Profits, and Lasting Value*, says that, when you increase the loyalty of your customer, **you can improve retention of the customer by 5 percentage points (say from 25 to 30 percent) and double your profit margin.** Yet the average business routinely loses 10 to 30% of their customers annually and the number one reason is "attitude of indifference from an employee." Simply said, the more loyal guests you can recruit and retain the higher your profits rise. It cost 5 times more to draw in a new guest as it does to keep a happy one coming back. Recent research says recruiting new customers may now cost 7-9 times the cost of serving an existing guest.

Loyal guests are your most profitable customers; they pay full price and know how to work best with you. If you are using coupons or discounts to draw diners to your restaurant, these people are not loyal and will disappear as soon as another establishment offers a price incentive. Loyal diners like your food, and service and go out of their way to eat there and to spread the word to family, friends and business colleagues.

Reichheld states that the customer who shows up on the strength of a personal recommendation tends to be higher quality (more profitable and stays with your restaurant longer) than the customer responding to advertising. He states that some customers are inherently more loyal than others. The Food Allergy Awareness Institute research validates that finding. Allergic patrons prefer dining at an establishment they have been to where they were served by a knowledgeable staff who made sure special needs were met.

Reichheld states the first step in building loyalty-based growth is to find and keep the right guests who will remain loyal and become more profitable with each succeeding year. I agree. Here's one story about how loyal my family became when we found a restaurant that made dining with food allergies a pleasurable experience.

⌘⌘⌘⌘⌘

My family lived in Brooklyn, New York. My parents dreaded family visits to restaurants because so often it would turn into a nightmare with me becoming quite ill over some small amount of allergic ingredient accidentally consumed. At the time I was allergic to 60 different foods. My parents really enjoy Chinese food. They eventually found Joy Teang; a Chinese restaurant that created a special dish, Roast Pork and Water Chestnuts (not on the menu), served exclusively for me. To this day, my parents will go out of their way to visit the Joy Teang in Brooklyn or Albany, New York out of the loyalty created more than three decades ago. When we met other family members or friends, this was the restaurant my parents would always recommend. My parents would enjoy their meal knowing I could enjoy mine.

People with allergies can become ill from even a tiny portion of the allergen in their food. The chef at Joy Teang would make sure that the spatula, wok, etc. were free from egg, peanuts, nuts, chicken, MSG and other items that would cause an allergic reaction. I can't even begin to calculate the amount of money generated by my family and the word-of-mouth they provided this restaurant for over 30 years. That's what loyalty is all about— creating long-term partnerships.

Loyal customers repeatedly return to your restaurant. They recommend your establishment to others. They stay loyal and return over time. The loyal allergic customer often brings many others. Allergic diners are very careful about where they eat. When dining with friends, family or business associates, the allergic diner almost always gets to choose the establishment. Others will say, *"Since you're more limited in what you can eat, where would you like to go?"* **The loyal guest will generate sales for you many times higher than what they alone consume. And they will continue to do this as long as you treat them well and meet their special needs.**

If an allergic diner is taking a client or prospective client out for a meal, he or she wants to know that business is the primary focus and they don't want to waste time worrying about getting sick. It can be embarrassing, awkward and frustrating to have to ask the server many questions about the menu in the presence of someone you don't know well. An allergic diner will choose a "safe" restaurant where they can order with confidence. They feel this way when on a date or celebrating a special event as well. Hmm, pretty much every time they go out.

Some restaurants take pride in serving their customer's special meals and meet or exceed the guest's expectations. China Doll, a large Chinese restaurant in Phoenix, is such a place. My CPA suggested lunch there and ordered items that weren't on the menu. He's a regular and brings them lots of business.

After explaining my food allergies we were immediately impressed with the server's "no problem" attitude. Each time there I specifically requested "no MSG, no egg," and the staff took great care of me. A year later, it seemed like a natural and fun idea to book their banquet room for my wedding reception and dinner for 200 people. We had a delicious, safe food and everyone was happy.

About the same time, I served as program chair of a state association and I chose to hold our Awards Banquet at China Doll (and the following year), bringing the restaurant another 120 diners. I personally introduced a minimum of 320 people to the establishment in less than two years. That doesn't count the fact that I've been telling positive stories about them for years. Do you know what that kind of promotion or publicity would cost?

The ONLY reason they got any of this business was because they treated me well and took care of my specific needs during lunch there that very first time.

Oh, by the way, many of those 320 people went back on their own, introducing their family, friends and colleagues to the restaurant. More than nine years later, people are still talking about the good time and great food we had at China Doll. And China Doll is still serving them flavorful food with great, safe service.

Customer loyalty is not the same as customer satisfaction. You may have many satisfied diners but that doesn't necessarily mean they will come back or tell others. Loyalty goes beyond satisfaction to create a stronger bond. With the allergic diner, it may be strengthened by the fact you've gone out of your way to create a memorable, safe dining experience for them. In *Understanding Your Customers* by Amanda Prus and D. Randall Brandt, Ph.D., they note that "In specialty markets where the product is tailored or customized for the customer, loyalty index scores tend to be higher than general or non-customized markets."

Chic consumers are quite adventurous with their dining habits. When a new restaurant opens, some people will immediately want to try it. Others wait for a friend or restaurant critic to give the place a favorable review before trying it out. The allergic diner is much more hesitant to try a new establishment. Fear keeps them away, it might make them sick. They are also more leery about new servers who may not be as familiar with the ingredients or as well trained to check with a chef or manager when in doubt.

This increased risk factor plays a part in the loyalty of returning repeatedly to places that serve them well.

> If you are willing to customize to meet the needs of this market, you might want to put a small note on the menu to that effect. "If you have special dietary needs, please alert the staff so we can meet your needs."

You are building a loyal customer base by specifically meeting your guest's special requirements. Allergic diners will share this information with each other and spread the word to others without dietary restrictions as well. There are food allergy networking groups, Celiac groups and others that meet in person and on line to share information about places that treat them well.

Many restaurants seem to consider it a hassle to deal with special requests. What was truly terrific about China Doll was their willingness to make tasty fried rice without egg. The kitchen staff went a step further and made sure the wok and utensils was thoroughly scrubbed so my meal wasn't contaminated with any small morsel of egg left from a previous order. They did this because they knew that even a rice size piece of allergen could cause severe illness or death to someone who is highly allergic.

> Restaurants that want repeat business and guest loyalty play it safe and follow the customer's request to the letter. If the server is unclear, the manager or chef speaks with the guest to ensure there is no miscommunication.

In a Greek/Italian restaurant with an extensive menu, every time Pat asked the server about a menu item, she would dutifully go to the kitchen and check. At the bottom of the menu it said "no substitutions" and the owner/chef enforced the edict. He would not modify anything as it would "ruin the dish." After the waitress made seven trips to the kitchen and Pat found nothing acceptable, he left and never returned. Not once did the owner/chef offer a suggestion of a palatable option.

Of course, he makes sure to share that story with others so they won't frequent a restaurant where the presentation is more important that the health of the guest.

Chapter 11
Superstar Customer Service

The customer may not always be right, but he is always the one with the money. To be most successful, a restaurant needs to provide excellent customer service, good food and a clean establishment. Treating people who have food allergies well should just be one of the many things you do to delight your guests. Without them, you wouldn't be in business.

Theodore Levitt says, *"Expectations are what people buy, not things."* Guests want to eat at restaurants that provide personalized service and perceived value. Service, especially "delicious" service for people with allergies, is remembered long after the price is forgotten.

"Slipshod service, mediocre meals, bad atmosphere, and poor value are driving away diners at an 'alarming rate'," according to a three-year study conducted by Feltenstein Partners, a restaurant

marketing consulting firm. On average, 7% of nearly 50,000 patrons polled said they would never return to the same restaurant because of lousy service or other woes. That portion rose to 12% for customers in upscale steakhouses or gourmet eateries. A separate study of 29,000 restaurant employees was even more damning. Almost half would not recommend their own restaurant as somewhere good to eat.

Do you believe you work for the best business of its kind in your area? If not, bet you wished you did! Being the best means doing many things right and at the top of the list it means providing great customer service. If you are not serving the guest well, you may not be in business long enough to accomplish other objectives because a dissatisfied diner tells 8 to 20 others of the negative experience and it takes a lot of advertising money to overcome this toxic word-of-mouth. **It takes 12 positive service incidents to overcome one negative one.** Yet, most dissatisfied guests won't even give you a second chance. And a guest who became sick sure isn't going to try you again.

Let's look at some tips that can make you provide the best service in your area.

❖ **Make every guest feel like a VIP, (very important patron) including the ones with food allergies and other special needs.** People will choose to dine where they feel important and appreciated.

For example, as a regular at the Gourmet Wok, a small takeout Chinese place with great food and great service, they took the time to learn my name and my dietary needs and preferences. I was always greeted by name and asked if I wanted "the usual," fried rice without egg and Hunan pork, extra spicy. They treated me like a VIP even though I requested modifications to their existing menu items.

How do you treat your regulars? Do you have families, groups of friends or business associates that dine frequently at your restaurant? Do you have associations that meet weekly or monthly at your location? Do you treat them well? Do you offer a pleasant greeting and go the extra mile or do you take the business for granted? The amount of spin off business you can book is incredible if you offer great service and treat each diner well.

❖ **Be easy to do business with.**
Guests go to a restaurant for an enjoyable experience so make it easy for them to select yours, again and again.

Another thing that makes Gourmet Wok a favorite spot is the philosophy of the owner, Tom. He says customers come in many different shapes and sizes and he doesn't want to offend any of them. He makes dining out easy. For that reason, his menu does not say "no substitutions," instead he will make what you want even if it is not on the menu. Tom says, "If you come here and want stir fry beef with vegetables, no soy sauce, I'll make it for you."

A growing number of diners prefer vegetarian meals. What options do you provide? If you're a caterer or a banquet manager, do you determine the number of veggie plates in advance or do you scurry at the last minute and throw something together? More hotels and restaurants are working with meeting planners to ensure that a vegetarian option exists and people can pre-register for this choice. This makes it much easier for everyone involved.

Is your menu guest-friendly or forbidding?

❖ **Always exceed your customers' expectations.**
Don't make promises you can't deliver.

As Nelson Boswell said, *"Here is a simple but powerful rule...always give people more than they expect to get."*

The difference between ordinary service and extraordinary service is a little extra effort. And it's that "little extra" that ensures repeat and referral business comes from delighted guests. Be imaginative, gracious and helpful. Train employees to cross department lines and work together to resolve guest concerns.

If a server doesn't know the ingredients in a product provided by a supplier, the manager then calls the supplier on the spot to get an answer.

If you go the distance for guests, you create lifetime customers, who'll tell others of their savory experience.

There are other benefits of providing great service. The first and most obvious one is that your paycheck depends on your customer! The more guests, the bigger your paycheck. Some businesses are strictly out for the money. Your restaurant is much more profitable when your business is based on repeat business from patrons who know what you offer and enjoy it. Money spent on advertising and discounts to consistently draw in new customers cuts into your profits.

Did you know the typical business only hears from 4% of its dissatisfied customers, 96% just go away, 91% never come back.

Can you afford to lose any business this year? Can you live on a smaller paycheck? If not, it's time to modify your thinking and start planning for success. If you provide great customer service, diners will come back. This is especially true for diners with special needs because they want to eat where they know they will be well cared for.

Another benefit of providing outstanding customer service is that you can use service as a selling tool—emphasize value! The legendary service providers are not the lowest-priced in their field. They tend toward the higher end. People are willing to pay more when they feel they are receiving value in return.

A third benefit of providing excellent customer service is that you retain existing customers. Most businesses spend their time attracting new business rather than in pleasing existing customers. Profitability is enhanced with each percentage increase in customer retention.

Employees take more pride in their jobs and develop a rapport or connection with the guests when they provide excellent service. In addition, it saves the restaurant the expense of continually having to hire and train new employees...An ongoing headache in the hospitality industry.

How Can You Provide Memorable Customer Service?

Focus on total quality

It's what makes businesses successful. People want to eat at those restaurants that have systems, processes and philosophies in place to consistently do the job right. This results in increased customer and employee satisfaction as well as decreased waste. Total quality is as crucial to the health of your guests as it is to the company that manufactures airplanes. One error can be deadly. Many communities are now publishing the health inspector's restaurant review scores in the newspaper or making the information available online. Are you proud of your scores?

Listen carefully and think

Many times your mind is anticipating ques-
tions and you don't hear what is really being
said. When Jim gets to a convention, he calls
the catering manager and says, *"Hi, I'm here
for the conference and I have some severe food
allergies. I would like to go over the menu with
you to be sure there are no items which have wheat, gluten or nuts
in the ingredients."* Often, the person on the other end of the
phone says, *"You're having Chicken Parmesan." "Thanks but that
doesn't help,"* Jim replies. *"I need to know if the chicken is breaded
and, if so, do the breadcrumbs contain wheat? I will be violently ill
if I eat even a very small amount of wheat."*

If the person had really been listening, she would have checked
the ingredients for the entire meal since Jim made her aware that
even a tiny bite of an allergen spells disaster (with potential legal
ramifications.) Unfortunately, the catering manager doesn't
check beyond the entrée and the serving staff does not know if
the salad dressing, au gratin potatoes or dessert contains wheat.

Ask appropriate questions

Probe to find out exactly what the guest can't
consume. Some vegetarians won't eat eggs or
dairy products. Some identify themselves as
vegans others don't. Others will eat fish and a
few only want organic produce. Just because
somebody says they want a vegetarian meal,
don't assume you know exactly what that
means.

If a diner says they do not want MSG in their meal, check to see if
the item contains hydrolyzed vegetable protein or other items
that contain MSG. See Chapter 1. If a server isn't 100% positive
of the ingredients, they should ask the chef or check the recipe
rather than to rely on their memory—too much is at stake.

All recipes, recipe cards and vendor ingredients should be in a central location. Everything served should be accounted for, including breads, desserts and anything else outsourced from vendors. If you are worried about the recipe for your "secret sauce" being jeopardized, limit access to the recipe to two trustworthy people per shift. If the recipe is guarded like the Coca-Cola recipe, then you have two options.

❖ One—Have someone with recipe access review Chapter 1 and compile a list that says if the dish contains any of the "Big Eight" allergens.

❖ Two—see below.

When in doubt, always tell customer not to eat an item

If the chef is not available or if the item was purchased from a supplier and no ingredients list is available, tell the diner that you don't know whether the item contains the allergen, then suggest a meal that is safe. Treat as though it is life threatening because it has the potential to be. You may be saving a life and developing a loyal customer who will bring you future business and referrals.

Offer appropriate substitutes

Make the guest feel valued and suggest an appropriate substitute. Guaranteed, they will remember you and speak highly of you. They will bring you business when there is an opportunity. For example, serving on three local committees provides the ability to impact decisions. When planning events, meetings and fundraisers, I lobby to avoid locations that have caused illness and negative experiences and favor those venues that serve well.

Recently a vegetarian friend was in charge of three conventions with more than 3,000 attendees. She certainly wanted to make sure that there were vegetarian options at every meal over the 10-day duration of the conventions. She chose the national chain that was best able to make sure that each property would provide high quality food for carnivores, food sensitive and vegetarian members alike. The events were very well received.

Treat your guests well and you'll increase your profits, customer loyalty and ensure the safety of your diners.

Resources

Web Sites

The Asthma and Allergy Information & Research
Www.users.globalnet.co.uk/~aair/nuts.htm

The Anaphylaxis Campaign
www.anaphylaxis.org.uk

Allerex – Epi-pen manufacturer www.allerex.ca

Celiac Disease Foundation
13251 Ventura Blvd. Suite 1, Studio City, CA 91604
818-990-2354
www.celiac.org

Celiac Sprue Association / United States of America
PO Box 31700
Omaha, NE 68131
402-558-0600
www.csaceliacs.org

Site offers a library of information for Celiac sufferers with links to other related sites

www.Celiac.com/forbiden.html
Scott Adam's site lists safe and forbidden foods

Food Allergy Survivors Together (FAST)
www.angelfire.com/sys/popup_source.shtml?Category=

Milk allergies
www.non-dairy.org

www.foodsubs.com/Flournw.html discusses food substitutions

National Jewish Medical and Research Center "Anaphylaxis" section www.njc.organization/MFhtml?ANA_MF.html

Food Products

'Cause You're Special Company
P.O. Box 316, Phillips, WI 54555
815-877-6722
www.causeyourespecial.com provides gluten-free baking mixes.

Dietary Specialties A Division of MenuDirect Corp.
865 Centennial Ave., Piscataway, NJ 08854
888-MENU123
www.dietspec.com

Sells gluten-free food products such as breakfast items, entrees, desserts and baking mixes that are produced in a gluten free facility.

Gillians Foods
462 Proctor Ave.
Revere MA 02151
781-286-4095

Provides gluten-free, lactose-free rolls, bread crumbs, pizza dough and garlic bread.

www.glutenfreemall.com provides over 900 products from 20 vendors that contain gluten-free, wheat-free, soy-free, egg-free, dairy-free and casein-free foods, at one Internet site.

The Gluten-Free Pantry Inc.
PO Box 840
Glastonbury, CT 06033
800-291-8386
www.glutenfree.com

Books and Cookbooks

Igoe, Robert, Hui, Y.H. *Dictionary of Food Ingredients*, 1996.

The *Dictionary of Food Ingredients* lists the components for various products and can be an invaluable reference tool.

Savill, Antoinette. *The Sensitive Gourmet – Imaginative Cooking without Dairy, Wheat or Gluten*

There are many cookbooks that cater specifically to people with food allergies. They can be found in libraries, bookstores and on the Internet. Visit www.fdalrgy.com to see books, you can click direct to order.

Safety Products

Health Safe Buffet System provides products to keep your buffet safer, minimizing germs and cross contamination.

954-564-8993 or www.safefoodsystems.com

National Restaurant Association, Food Allergy poster for your kitchen, order two as the reverse side is in Spanish.

800-424-5156

Vinyl gloves, SmartPractice, 3400 E. McDowell Rd., Phoenix, AZ 85008 or call 800-552-0800

Other Products

"Master Chef" is a computerized recipe system that can provide nutritional analysis, can print out ingredients, carbohydrates, fat, etc. This may be useful to those thinking about modifying their menus.

Other Information Sources on Food Allergies

Allergy and Asthma Network/Mothers of Asthmatics, Inc.
3554 Chain Bridge Road, Suite 200
Fairfax, VA 22030
(702) 385-4403
www.podi.com/health/aanma/

American Academy of Allergy and Immunology
611 East Wells Street
Milwaukee, WI 53202
(414) 272-6071 or
Allergy Information Line 1-800-822-2762
www.aaaai.organization/index.html

American College of Allergy and Immunology
800 East Northwest Hwy, Suite 1080
Palatine, IL 60067

Asthma and Allergy Foundation of America
1125 15th Street, NW, Suite 502
Washington, DC 2005
1-800-727-8462

Food Allergy Awareness Institute
5418 E. Anderson Dr., Scottsdale, AZ 85254
877-332-5749
www.fdalrgy.com

Helping restaurants and other food service providers learn how to safely serve allergic guests.

Food Allergy and Anaphylaxis Network
4744 Holly Avenue
Fairfax, VA 22030
(703) 691-3179
www.foodallergy.org

National Institute of Allergy and Infectious Diseases
9000 Rockville Pike, Bldg. 7A-32
Bethesda, MD 20892
(301) 496-5717

References

Articles, Magazines or Web sites

Aan de Brugh, Marcel. "Genetically Engineered Secret Ingredients." *World Press Review* Feb. 2000:p. 40-41.

The American Academy of Allergy, Asthma and Immunology. "Adverse Reactions to Foods." May, 1995.

The American Academy of Allergy, Asthma and Immunology. "Understanding Food Allergy." May 1993.

The American Academy of Allergy, Asthma and Immunology. "Restaurants Paying Attention to Food Allergy Lawsuits." 1997.

"Certain Foods Can Provoke Asthma Symptoms in Adults." *American Family Physician*, Feb. 15, 2000:p. 1108.

The Anaphylaxis Campaign Website. *Anaphylaxis Campaign Newsletter* Feb. 2000.

The Anaphylaxis Campaign Website. "Guidance for Caterers"

Asthma & Allergy Information & Research Website. "Nut Allergy – The Basics"

Barron, James. "Dear Mr. Carver. This is a Cease and Desist Order." *New York Times* Sept 27, 1998.

Breuhaus, Brian. "Proceed with Caution." *Restaurant Business* July 1, 1998:p. 27.

Bolton, Lance. "A Case for Food Safety." *Restaurant Hospitality* July 1997:p. 122-126.

California Restaurant Association Special Report. "Serving Customers with Food Allergies" Nov. 1997.

Collier Cool, Lisa. "Is There Celery in That Tuna?" *Good Housekeeping* Feb. 2000.

Dodell, David D.M.D. *Medical Sciences Bulletin* Aug. 31, 1995.

Doheny, Kathleen. "Airline Policy on Peanuts is Mixed Bag after DOT Raised Allergy Concerns." *Los Angeles Times* Dec. 13, 1998:p. 112.

Dulen, Jacqueline. "Food Safety, Three Ways." *Restaurants and Institutions* March 15, 1998.

Elder, John; Sallis, James; Zive; Michelle, Hoy, Patricia:

Evers, William. "Food Allergies – EFR 6-21." *Electronic Food Rap* May 1996.

FDA Backgrounder Monosodium Glutamate (MSG) Oct. 1991.

Fitzpatrick, M. Patricia; Chapman, Gwen; Barr, Susan. "Lower-fat menu items in restaurants satisfy customers." *Journal of the American Dietetic Association* May 1997:pp 510-514.

"Research Update: Prevalence of Peanut and Tree Nut Allergy in the United States." *Food Allergy News* April – May 1999:p. 10.

Food Insight, "Food Allergy: The Dangers of "Wait and See"", Sept/Oct. 1992

Foulke, Judith. "Nutrition Information on Restaurant Menus." *Food & Drug Administration Talk Paper* July 30, 1996.

Grindy, Bruce. "Restaurants Build Loyalty Among Seniors and Families." *Restaurants USA* March 1998:pp. 45-6.

Green, Michelle. "The Food Hangover." *Wall Street Journal* Nov. 20, 1998:p. W1.

Hamann, Curtis. "Natural Rubber Latex Protein Sensitivity in Review." *American Journal of Contact Dermatitis* Vol. 4, No 1 (March) 1993:pp. 4-21.

Hamann, Curtis. "Natural Rubber Latex Hypersensitivity: Incidence and Prevalence of Type I Allergy in the Dental Profession." *Journal of the American Dental Association* Jan. 1998. pp. 43-54.

Hunter, Beatrice Trum. "Food Allergies: No Trivial Health Matter." *Consumers Research* Feb. 1999:pp. 21-26.

Hutchcraft, Chuck. "Up to Snuff Onging Employee Training Sharpens Skills and Competitive Edge." *Restaurants & Institutions* Aug. 15, 1999:pp. 93-98.

Hutchcraft, Chuck, Hume, Scott; Matsumoto, Janice; Sheridan, Margaret; Waters, Jennifer. "Meat Alert." *Restaurants & Institutions* Oct, 1, 1999:p. 24.

International Food Information Council Foundation, "Everything You Need to Know about Glutamate and Monosodium Glutamate." Jan. 1997.

Kemp, Stephen; Lockey, Richard; Glaros, Timothy. "Peanut Anaphylaxis From Food Cross-Contamination." *Journal of the American Medical Association* June 5, 1996:pp. 1636-7.

Koppelman, Stef J.; Wensing, Marjolein; de Jong, Govardus A H; Knulst, Andre C. "Anaphylaxis caused by the unexpected presence of casein in salmon." *The Lancet* Dec. 18, 1999:p. 2136.

Kurtzweil, Paula. "Today's Special: Nutrition Information." *FDA Consumer Magazine* May-June 1997.

Lagnado, Lucette. "Chefs at the Biotech Barricades." *Wall Street Journal* March 9, 2000:p. B1.

Leung, Donald, M.D.; Bock, Allan M.D. National Jewish Medical and Research Center. "Food Allergy" – from web site

Levine, Ed. "Kid-Friendly Eateries with NO Golden Arches," *Business Week* March 29, 1999:pp. 191-2.

Lindner, Lawrence. "A Dinner Date with Danger," *Washington Post* Feb. 16, 1999:p. WH20.

Lord, Mary. "There's a fly in my soup." *U.S. News & World Report* Nov. 22, 1999:p. 53.

Lowe, Kimberly D. "Take Inspiration Higher" *Restaurants & Institutions* Sept 1, 1997.

Marcus, Mary Brophy. "Heart Healthy? Restaurant Fare." *U.S. News & World Report*, April 28, 1997:p 70.

Marshall, Anthony. "Allergy Sufferers Itching to Inform Foodservice Industry" *Hotel & Motel Management* May 6, 1998:pp. 19 & 61.

Marshall, Anthony. "Food Allergies are Nothing to Sneeze at." *Hotel & Motel Management* Feb. 6, 1995:p. 11.

Marshall, Anthony. "Hotel Restaurants Should Design Menus With Guests in Mind." *Hotel & Motel Management* Jan. 12, 1998:pp. 30 & 36.

Matus, Jordan. "Ever Been Threatened by a Nut?" *Prevention* Oct. 1999:p. 39.

Mayo Clinic. *Food Allergy Prevention: Reading Labels* Dec. 21, 1999.

Mayo Clinic. *Food Allergies and Travel: Prevent on the Road Reactions* Nov. 16, 1999.

Mayo Clinic. *Seafood Allergies: Prevention calls for Planning* Sept. 14, 1999.

McKenzie, Thomas; Nader, Philip; Berry, Charles. "Factors Affecting Selection of Restaurants by Anglo and Mexican-American families." *Journal of the American Dietetic Association.* July 1999:p. 856.

Moncreiff Arrarte, Anne. "8 Foods Cause 90 percent of Allergic Reactions." *The Star-Ledger* Aug. 25, 1998:p. 11.

Motala, Cassim, Dr. *Allergy Society of South Africa Handbook.*

Mulheri, Kim Esq. "Bakery Suit Settled." *Food Allergy News* Dec. 1999: p 11.

National Restaurant Association, "What You Need to Know About Food Allergies." 1992.

"Muslims file suit against Denny's." *Nation's Restaurant News* Feb. 1, 1999:p. 4.

"To Build Traffic, Think 'Service'." *Nation's Restaurant News* Dec. 20, 1999:p. 16.

NoMSG Web site.

Notar, Robert. "Radisson Leader Directs Brand Growth." *Hotel & Motel Management* Jan. 12, 1998:p. 61.

Palmer, Jeannette; Leontos, Carolyn. "Nutritional Training for Chefs: Taste as an Essential Determinant of Choice." *Journal of the American Dietetic Association* Dec. 1995:pp. 1418-1421.

Papazian, Ruth. "Sulfites: Safe for Most, Dangerous for Some." *FDA Consumer Magazine* Dec. 1996.

Papiernik, Richard. "A Cork on Litigation? You Still Have to Buy the Cork!" *Nation's Restaurant News* Oct. 27, 1997:p. 11.

Peraino, Kevin. "The Perils of Pasta: As many as 1 million Americans may have an intolerance for gluten, an ingredient in more foods than you think." *Newsweek* Oct. 11, 1999:p. 89.

Petersen, Andrea. "Surf & Serve: Leading Chefs Pick their Favorite Food Sites" *Wall Street Journal* Feb. 9, B8.

Piantadosi, Roger. "Deciphering Airline Veggie Meals is Eggs-Acting Science" *Los Angeles Times* May 24, 1998:p. L2.

Pumphrey, Richard S. "Epinephrine-resistant Food Anaphylaxis." *The Lancet Ltd* March 25, 2000.

Prus, Amanda and Brandt, D. Randall Ph.D. "Understanding Your Customers." *Marketing Tools Magazine* July/August 1995.

Regenstein, Ph.D. "Are 'Pareve' Products Really Milk-Free?" *Food Allergy News* August-September 1998:pp. 1, 7.

Reichler, Gayle and Dalton, Sharron. "Chef's attitudes toward healthful food preparation are more positive than their food science knowledge and practices." *Journal of the American Dietetic Association* Feb. 1998.

"Data Tracking 99% of food related illnesses aren't reported." *Restaurant Business Magazine* July 1, 1998:pp. 32-3.

"Frequent Diners Keep Coming Back for More." *Restaurant Industry Forecast* 1998.

Ronan, Courtney. "Dallas Child Found a Peanut: Dangerous Food Allergies." Family.com.

Rousseau, Rita. "Food Safety for the Few: Ordinary foods can be poison for people with allergies." *Restaurants & Institutions* Feb. 1, 1997:p. 78.

Sherman, Chatzky, Jean. "Send It Back: When you eat out, don't be afraid to demand your rights." *Money* Oct. 1999:p. 208.

Silver, Deborah. "Active Service: As far as consumers are concerned, a little respect goes a long way." *Restaurants & Institutions* Feb. 15, 2000:pp. 38-44.

Smith, Melissa Diane. "Dealing with Food Allergies." *Delicious!* Jan. 1997:pp. 16-19.

"Your child & peanuts – coping with an anaphylactic food allergy." *Sully's Living Without Magazine: A Lifestyle Guide for People with Food and Chemical Sensitivities* Spring 1998:pp. 42-44.

Sussman, Gordon; Yang, William. "When Sulfites pose a hidden danger." *Consultant*, Dec. 1998:p 2834.

"Nothing to Sneeze At: Manufacturers Rush to Develop 'Allergy-Free' Foods" *Trends in Japan* Sept. 16, 1997.

Wien, M. Jill. "Creating Sensational Special Meals." *The Meeting Professional* June 1998:pp. 100-112.

Williams, Lisa. "Tuning the Right Frequency: Incentive programs jump-start sales and customer loyalty." *Restaurants & Institutions* Oct. 1, 1999:pp. 76-82.

Wilkinson, Sophie. "Deconstructing Food Allergies: What makes an allergen an allergen?" *Chemical and Engineering News* Sept. 7, 1998.

Wolfe, David B. "What Your Customers Can't Say." *American Demographics* Feb. 1998.

Yee, Laura. "Venerable Vegetarian: Meatless meals demand respect as interest in fresh food and healthy eating grows." *Restaurants and Institutions* Dec. 1, 1999:pp. 28-40.

Yost, Barbara. "Big Flavors, Big taste: Chef shares tips on heart-healthy fare." *The Arizona Republic* 1998.

Zeiger, Robert S, MD, PhD. Research Update: Peanut and Tree Nut Survey and Status of Immunomodulation, Aug. 15, 1998.

Books

Bhote, Keki. *Beyond Customer Satisfaction to Customer Loyalty.* 1996.

Charlesworth, Ernest N. *Cutaneous Allergy.*

Griffin, Jill. *Customer Loyalty, How to Earn it, How to Keep it.* 1995.

Heskett, James. *The Service Profit Chain: How Leading Companies Link Profit and Growth to Loyalty, Satisfaction.*

Igoe, Robert, Hui, Y.H. *Dictionary of Food Ingredients.* 1996.

National Restaurant Association. *What You Need to Know About Food Allergies.* 1995.

National Restaurant Association Educational Foundation, *ServSafe Essentials,* 1999.

Natural Rubber Latex Hypersensitivities Chapter by Hamann, Curtis and Sullivan, Kim.

Raphel, Murray, *Up the Loyalty Ladder, Turning Sometime Customers into Fulltime Advocates for your Business.* 1995.

Reichheld, Frederick. *The Loyalty Effect: The Hidden Force Behind Growth, Profits and Lasting Value.* 1996.

Winter, Ruth. *Consumer's Dictionary of Food Additives.* 1989.

Index

T

W